Bumper
PUB
Quiz Book

COSMO BROWN

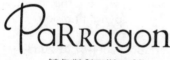

Bath · New York · Cologne · Melbourne · Delhi
Hong Kong · Shenzhen · Singapore · Amsterdam

This edition published by Parragon Books Ltd in 2014

Parragon Books Ltd
Chartist House
15–17 Trim Street
Bath BA1 1HA, UK
www.parragon.com

Produced and designed by Design Prinicipals, Warminster
Edited by Cosmo Brown
Cover design by Talking Design

ISBN 978-1-4723-7063-1
Printed in China

Contents

Introduction

QUIZZES 1–314

ANSWERS 1–314

Happy Fathers Day

Bumper PUB Quiz Book

With love
from Paul & Natalie.
xx

Introduction

The 5000-plus questions in this book are divided into 314 individual quizzes, specially devised for quiz nights at your local pub and elsewhere. The majority of the quizzes comprise a wide-ranging selection of general knowledge questions, with something to test everyone. In addition, for those who want to focus on a particular subject, there are a number of single-topic quizzes filtered through the book on Sport, Cinema and TV, Science and Nature, Music, History and Geography.

The answers to all the questions are handily grouped (though not too temptingly accessible) at the back of the book. Whether you are a regular quiz contestant or someone new to the game, the *Bumper Pub Quiz Book* will prove challenging, stimulating, entertaining and informative.

Of course you don't have to be in a pub or a bar to stage a quiz. But it helps – especially if the next question is 'Whose round is it?'

Good luck!

QUIZ 1

① Who was the UK prime minister when World War Two ended?

② What is a saraband?

③ Which famous P&O ship entered service in 1961?

④ What, in nautical terms, is a spanker?

⑤ Name the salad made of mixed diced vegetables and mayonnaise.

⑥ Who is the slave girl in *Ali Baba and the Forty Thieves*?

⑦ Who composed the Goldberg Variations?

⑧ Which Russian dissident won the Nobel Peace Prize in 1975?

⑨ What relation was Terry-Thomas to Richard Briers?

⑩ What do the initials in A A Gill stand for?

⑪ What word can follow black, fire or jail?

⑫ What does the word gospel mean?

⑬ How many cents make a nickel?

⑭ What are 'angels on horseback'?

⑮ Who composed the *Neighbours* theme tune?

⑯ What was poet Philip Larkin's day job?

QUIZ 2

① What does RCM stand for?

② What is a crambo: an exotic dance, fruit drink or word game?

③ What is Norwich City FC's home ground?

④ Whose 1999 hit was 'Boom, Boom, Boom, Boom!'?

⑤ What is shrub?

⑥ Who owned Bagpuss?

⑦ Whose first novel was *High Fidelity*?

⑧ What relation was Napoleon III to Napoleon I?

⑨ How many non-permanent members are on the UN Security Council?

⑩ Which famous Russian writer died at a railway station?

⑪ What is the name of David Cameron's wife?

⑫ How many quavers in a crotchet?

⑬ What type of creature is a cuttlefish?

⑭ What were the surnames of Bonnie and Clyde?

⑮ Which fraternal pop trio publicly forswore sex before marriage?

⑯ What is a female swan called?

QUIZ 3

1. What was Harold Wilson's political constituency?

2. What railway station has the most platforms in the world?

3. Who is holding a trumpet on the 'Sgt Pepper' album cover?

4. Which chicken dish is named after a US state?

5. Who was the Roman goddess of corn?

6. What is the opera *La Gazza Ladra* called in English?

7. What is the largest gland in the human body?

8. Which prominent Lib Dem is a dedicated ballroom dancer?

9. What is William Gladstone's middle name?

10. Which George was Flash Harry at St Trinian's?

11. When is Prince William's birthday?

12. Who was the first star of a talking movie?

13. How many capital cities does South Africa have?

14. In which country would you find a carpetbag steak?

15. Name the other half: Troilus and . . .

16. Paris is divided into how many *arrondissements*?

QUIZ 4

① What does P&O stand for?

② Who died first, Bud Abbott or Lou Costello?

③ In which street does the Addams Family live?

④ What was the priestess at Delphi's Temple of Apollo called?

⑤ What was Alec Guinness' first film as a featured actor?

⑥ Which Nigerian state broke away as a republic in 1967?

⑦ What is a ruffe?

⑧ Which US-born poet won the Nobel Prize for Literature in 1948?

⑨ Temple Meads is which city's principal railway station?

⑩ How many masts does a ketch have?

⑪ What is comedian Paul Merton's real name?

⑫ In which year was Prince Harry born?

⑬ Which of the Seven Dwarfs is of a retiring disposition?

⑭ Who wrote the 1992 novel *The English Patient*?

⑮ What is Lascaux in France famous for?

⑯ What is Australia's national anthem?

QUIZ 5

① Which South American dictator died in 2006?

② Which London department store first opened its doors in 1909?

③ What was the Queen Mother's maiden name?

④ Budgerigars are native to which country?

⑤ What is a more familiar term for a tonsorial artist?

⑥ What brand was promoted as 'The Beer That Men Drink'?

⑦ Who is the creator of Captain Horatio Hornblower?

⑧ What loses its toes when swimming in the Bristol Channel?

⑨ Which George was a famous governor of Alabama?

⑩ What nationality was St Thomas Aquinas?

⑪ Who was the first male to appear on the cover of *Playboy*?

⑫ Cool, Nice and Oz are all what?

⑬ Who wrote the James Bond novel, *Devil May Care*?

⑭ What did Jacob Schick invent in 1928?

⑮ What is 1939 in Roman numerals?

⑯ What does the Internet chat initials BWL stand for?

QUIZ 6

① What is a hot-air balloon's basket called?

② Who was the first US president to wear contact lenses?

③ Who composed the *Peer Gynt Suite*?

④ In which month is Epiphany?

⑤ What is chewing gum traditionally made from?

⑥ Jerry Springer is a former mayor of which city?

⑦ What do Americans call a cupboard?

⑧ What was the artist Kandinsky's first name?

⑨ Who, in 2008, became the first celebrity gay divorcee?

⑩ Who wrote *The Battle of the Books*?

⑪ How is food *en brochette* served?

⑫ In which city is the Juilliard School of Music?

⑬ Which military leader's horse was named Marengo?

⑭ Who refereed the 2010 FIFA World Cup Final?

⑮ Who was Henry VIII's third wife?

⑯ How many arms does a cuttlefish have?

QUIZ 7

① What nationality was Mother Theresa?

② What heroic feat did Cpt Chesley Sullenberger perform in 2009?

③ In which year was the first email sent?

④ Does an insect have an internal or external skeleton?

⑤ What dental feature was invented in 1817?

⑥ Which region of Scotland contains the most whisky distilleries?

⑦ What is the chemical name for saltpetre?

⑧ In what country is the Angkor Archaeological Park?

⑨ What was London's Tate Modern in its former life?

⑩ Which ball game occupies the largest playing area?

⑪ What were kiwi fruits originally called?

⑫ In the Royal Navy what rank is 'Jimmy the One'?

⑬ In World War Two, what was the 7th Armoured Division known as?

⑭ What is a corncrake?

⑮ Which motorway links Liverpool and Hull?

⑯ In which opera by Mozart are Fiordiligi and Dorabella?

QUIZ 8
SPORT

1. Which country is scheduled to host the 2015 Rugby World Cup?

2. How many lanes has an Olympic-sized swimming pool?

3. What does 'TT' stand for in the Isle of Man TT Race?

4. What are 'zippers' to an American footballer?

5. Which of Bristol's two major football clubs is oldest, City or Rovers?

6. Who was the first woman to run a mile in under five minutes?

7. What sporting weapon fires a quarrel?

8. Who succeeded Ian Botham as England cricket captain in 1981?

9. Who was the first professional footballer to be knighted?

10. In which year did Jenson Button win his first Grand Prix?

11. What is the oldest domestic football cup competition?

12. How many points is a blue ball worth in snooker?

13. What is the venue for the US Tennis Open?

14. How many oars are used in sculling?

15. Which sport featured in the 1969 movie *Fat City*?

16. In golf, what is known as the 'dance floor'?

QUIZ 9

① Who was the creator of the *Mr Men* characters?

② Which Somerset town is synonymous with a type of carpet?

③ What does *tempus fugit* mean?

④ Which former US president won the Nobel Peace Prize in 2002?

⑤ What are cooked vegetables cut into fine strips called?

⑥ Where in China is the 'Forbidden City'?

⑦ What does quondam mean?

⑧ Arial, Geneva and Rockwell are all what?

⑨ Which saint's shrine is at Lourdes?

⑩ What was Margaret Thatcher's constituency?

⑪ In rugby union, what number shirt does the hooker wear?

⑫ Which is Holland's most exported cheese, Edam or Gouda?

⑬ What was the BBC World Service originally called?

⑭ What came first, the light bulb or telephone?

⑮ What part did Todd Carty play in *Grange Hill*?

⑯ Who was the 40th president of the USA?

QUIZ 10

① What is the town of Sèvres famous for?

② Who did Tony Blair succeed as leader of the Labour Party?

③ How did comedian Rod Hull die?

④ What is feta cheese made from?

⑤ How is the wild carrot better known in the UK?

⑥ Which country churchyard inspired Thomas Gray's famous elegy?

⑦ What was the chocolate Snicker bar previously called?

⑧ Apple pips contain what toxic substance?

⑨ When did Robbie Williams leave Take That: 1996, 1997 or 1998?

⑩ Which city is further south, Pisa or Florence?

⑪ How many parts to a triptych?

⑫ Which British male was nicknamed the 'Sex Thimble'?

⑬ What do the initials stand for in J K Rowling?

⑭ What does a durometer measure?

⑮ Which Cabinet minister swapped his wife for his secretary in 1997?

⑯ In which sport did Mike Hailwood win nine world titles?

QUIZ 11

① What does *prêt-à-porter* mean?

② The pop group Wet Wet Wet came from which country?

③ Which coffee bean contains the most caffeine, Arabica or Robusta?

④ What was the first Duke of Wellington's name?

⑤ Which fictional character returned from the dead in 1905?

⑥ Olympic gymnast Nadia Comaneci represented which country?

⑦ Blenheim Palace is in which English county?

⑧ In which year did Starbucks open its first UK branch?

⑨ Who became 'Chief of the French State' in 1940?

⑩ Who created Hanibal Lecter?

⑪ In the song, what was given on the 'Twelfth Day of Christmas'?

⑫ What word can follow black, boot or fine?

⑬ How many cents make a dime?

⑭ What does the rail service TGV stand for?

⑮ Which British MP claimed expenses for cleaning his moat?

⑯ What was the first car to have a fifth door?

QUIZ 12

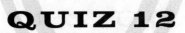

① In which European city is the Bridge of Sighs?

② What was the name of the so-called Yorkshire Ripper?

③ Emma Thompson won the 'Best Actress' Oscar for which 1993 film?

④ Which country won the rugby gold medal at the 1920 Olympics?

⑤ Who wrote the novel *The Naked and the Dead*?

⑥ Which fighter plane was nicknamed the 'Balalaika'?

⑦ The Suez Canal links which two seas?

⑧ How many pounds in a hundredweight?

⑨ Who blew the whistle on David Beckham, sex wise, in 2004?

⑩ Who is the patron saint of lost causes?

⑪ Where was Eddie Izzard born?

⑫ What was the first James Bond book?

⑬ Which British sculptor is noted for using natural materials?

⑭ What, methodically speaking, does MO stand for?

⑮ What is the logo of the upmarket apparel company Lacoste?

⑯ What was the name of the Brighton hotel bombed in 1984?

QUIZ 13

① Which sea is larger, Caribbean or Mediterranean?

② What species of bird is a Greylag?

③ What was the first pair of Doc Marten boots made from?

④ In which musical is Ensign Nellie Forbush a character?

⑤ A stygiophobic has a fear of what?

⑥ Which country was at war with itself from 1975 to 1991?

⑦ What do golfers use a niblick club for?

⑧ Which Italian film director was murdered in 1975?

⑨ What do the initials stand for in A A Milne?

⑩ Who wrote the poem 'Not Waving but Drowning'?

⑪ What was the name of Edward Heath's yacht?

⑫ In which year did Dr Who make his television debut?

⑬ Who succeeded Gerald Ford as US president in 1977?

⑭ Which actor was Joan Collins' first husband?

⑮ What tempo is a Viennese waltz?

⑯ Georges Seurat was an exponent of which style of painting?

QUIZ 14

① Where in the USA was the atom bomb developed?

② Which England cricketer was nicknamed 'Arkle'?

③ What is 'ie' short for?

④ What is the national anthem of the USA?

⑤ The Wars of the Roses were between which two royal houses?

⑥ 'Caesar and Cleo' was the original name of which singing duo?

⑦ Which Indian city has the largest population?

⑧ In which English city is Winson Green Prison?

⑨ Who was the first president of the French Fifth Republic?

⑩ In which year was the NHS launched?

⑪ What is the judicial capital of South Africa?

⑫ Who was the first-ever winner of *The X Factor*?

⑬ What is the common name for ethylene glycol?

⑭ Which singing star changed her name from Mary O'Brien?

⑮ In which county is the Isle of Wight?

⑯ What is Ian Botham's middle name?

QUIZ 15
CINEMA & TV

① Which film ends with the line: 'Nobody's perfect'?

② Who is Geraldine Granger?

③ Who played the Russell Crowe part in the original *3.10 to Yuma*?

④ In which film did Clint Eastwood go mountaineering?

⑤ What are the surnames of Bob and Terry in *The Likely Lads*?

⑥ Who is Tony Soprano's shrink?

⑦ What does the character Tarzan's name mean?

⑧ What was the original title for *Coronation Street*?

⑨ Who directed *Shallow Grave*?

⑩ What does *M*A*S*H* stand for?

⑪ Who is the older Bridges brother, Beau or Jeff?

⑫ Who played Dr Samuel Johnson in *Blackadder the Third*?

⑬ Which city is home to *Hollyoaks*?

⑭ *Family Plot* was which director's last film?

⑮ The film *Revolutionary Road* is based on whose novel?

⑯ Whose catchphrase was 'I am not a number, I am a free man.'

QUIZ 16

① What is the smallest state in the USA?

② Which Dennis created *The Singing Detective*?

③ What is a male witch called?

④ Which Irish playwright co-founded the London School of Economics?

⑤ Who played the title role in the TV sitcom *Rhoda*?

⑥ Which English cricket county's badge features three pears?

⑦ In Shakespeare's *The Tempest*, who is Miranda's father?

⑧ Which land measurement equals a quarter of an acre?

⑨ What is the largest species of penguin?

⑩ What in Japan was a *shogun*?

⑪ What does the musical term *adagio* mean?

⑫ What animal is featured on the Falkland Islands flag?

⑬ If you are ergophobic, what are you afraid of?

⑭ Who wrote the sci-fi classic *The Midwich Cuckoos*?

⑮ Which revolutionary arts movement was founded in 1916?

⑯ What was Norman Tebbit's job before he became an MP?

QUIZ 17

① Who was the first Bishop of Rome?

② Which former politician wrote the novel *A Parliamentary Affair*?

③ Tennis player Gustavo Kuerten is from which country?

④ Which English director made the film *Fatal Attraction*?

⑤ What is the first prime number?

⑥ 'Graded grains make finer flour' was which brand's slogan?

⑦ What is the nickname for the GCHQ building in Cheltenham?

⑧ Who composed *The Rite of Spring*?

⑨ Which sea separates Siberia and the USA?

⑩ Which West Indian cricketer was knighted in 1995?

⑪ By what other name is the *Mona Lisa* painting also known?

⑫ Which UK literary annual award was launched in 1969?

⑬ What does the variola virus cause?

⑭ Ermine comes from which animal?

⑮ Which presidential wife dated Eric Clapton and Mick Jagger?

⑯ With which city was graffiti artist Banksy first associated?

QUIZ 18

① What is 'eg' short for?

② Who was Denis Thatcher's second wife?

③ What flag is sometimes called 'The Red Duster'?

④ What animal provides cashmere wool?

⑤ Which Roman emperor's last words were 'I am still alive'?

⑥ What is the length of a full marathon in miles and yards?

⑦ Who plays Reuben Tishkoff in the film *Ocean's Eleven*?

⑧ How many King Louis's of France have there been?

⑨ Which city is 13 miles from Newmarket?

⑩ What is larger, 4/5th or 6/7th?

⑪ How many cards are needed to play Euchre?

⑫ What is the term for a wall painting?

⑬ Who wrote the best-selling novel *Man and Boy*?

⑭ Who did William Jefferson Blythe become?

⑮ Which sporting star fathered a child in a broom cupboard?

⑯ RANDOM ADVICE is an anagram of which politician's name?

QUIZ 19

① What is the smallest of the flute family?

② What was the name of Smokey Robinson's backing group?

③ In which field of the arts did Anton Dolin make his name?

④ What in radio terms does AM stand for?

⑤ Emeralds and aquamarines are varieties of which stone?

⑥ Which English poet became a Greek national hero?

⑦ Who succeeded James Callaghan as leader of the Labour Party?

⑧ How many players are there in an ice hockey team?

⑨ Dr Who is a Time Lord from which planet?

⑩ Which famous German battleship was sunk in November 1944?

⑪ What is the Roman road between London and York called?

⑫ What are the dots that make up a computer image?

⑬ Who said, 'I'm a Ford, not a Lincoln'?

⑭ What is the name for a human's upper jaw?

⑮ Where in Italy was Galileo Galilei born?

⑯ Hickstead is associated with which sport?

QUIZ 20

① With which city is the band Radiohead associated?

② What does a phillumenist collect?

③ What is the word for a cloud of gas and dust in space?

④ Who said: 'Genius is 99% perspiration and 1% inspiration'?

⑤ What is the resting place for drowned sailors called?

⑥ The name of which Middle Eastern capital means 'warm place'?

⑦ Who wrote the lyrics for the musical *Starlight Express*?

⑧ The US state of Virginia was named in honour of whom?

⑨ What is hard tack?

⑩ What, in sporting terms, does WSM stand for?

⑪ Who succeeded Hitler as leader of the Third Reich?

⑫ Which doctor was in love with Lara Antipova?

⑬ Bossa nova is a style of music from which country?

⑭ What does *bossa nova* mean?

⑮ What was Jane Austen's first published novel?

⑯ What do sculptors make as a preliminary model?

QUIZ 21

① Who was the founder of the FBI?

② Who did Mary Decker trip over at the 1984 Olympics?

③ For which film did Daniel Day-Lewis win his second Oscar?

④ Who said: 'Golf is a good walk spoiled'?

⑤ Which former US president died in June 1973?

⑥ How did Wyatt Earp die?

⑦ Sir Alan Cobham was a pioneer in which field?

⑧ David Sneddon was the first winner of which TV talent show?

⑨ Which French aviator has a sports stadium named after him?

⑩ Which mountain is home to Zeus and Hera?

⑪ In which year did Charles Dickens die: 1860, 1870 or 1880?

⑫ Which rock band's name is often shortened to CCR?

⑬ What type of power is aeolic?

⑭ In which year did the Edinburgh Festival first take place?

⑮ Who is older, Matt Lucas or David Walliams?

⑯ Name the only Eastern Bloc country to attend the LA Olympics.

QUIZ 22
SCIENCE & NATURE

① Which bird can swim but can't fly?

② Where in the human body do you find collagen?

③ How many stomachs has a cow?

④ Which metal has the highest melting point?

⑤ Which salad item is *Nasturtium officinale*?

⑥ What is the highest cloud formation?

⑦ What high-tech item can slide, swivel or flip?

⑧ What did James Hargreaves invent in 1764?

⑨ How is the European Organization for Nuclear Research better known?

⑩ What is a male swan called?

⑪ Capuchin, Howler and Spider are all types of what?

⑫ What is the common name for Magnesium sulphate?

⑬ Who wrote the environmental classic *The Silent Spring*?

⑭ Tornadoes in the Northern Hemisphere generally spin which way?

⑮ In how many years will the sun run out of fuel?

⑯ What is a falcon's nest called?

QUIZ 23

① Who sculpted the lions in London's Trafalgar Square?

② In which region of Spain is Seville?

③ Where did the kumquat originate?

④ Which 'royal' was 1971 BBC Sports Personality of the Year?

⑤ Which pier features in a George Orwell book title?

⑥ What, in nature, is a 'pelican's foot'?

⑦ Which Hollywood star was charged with murder in 1920?

⑧ Who played first-class cricket for 39 consecutive years?

⑨ Which Andrew Lloyd Webber musical is based on a 1950 film?

⑩ Which are more nutritious, white or brown eggs?

⑪ Russell Brand named his cat after which pop singer?

⑫ Who did Private Eye magazine christen 'The Grocer'?

⑬ Where did Jamie Oliver start his Ministry of Food campaign?

⑭ What is a *nun-cha-ku*?

⑮ Which ex-*Blue Peter* presenter became a vet in *Emmerdale*?

⑯ What does the Audi slogan *Vorsprung durch technik* mean?

QUIZ 24

① What is 777 in Roman numerals?

② What word can follow dead, dread and head?

③ *What You See Is What You Get* is the title of whose autobiography?

④ Which Flemish artist became court painter to Charles I?

⑤ Which owl is larger, snowy or tawny?

⑥ Who led the English cricket 'rebel' tour to South Africa in 1989?

⑦ Which TV cook did Phyllis Primrose-Pechey become?

⑧ What does the Latin word *ergo* mean?

⑨ Which US state did the Bee Gees sing about in 1967?

⑩ In physics, Q is the symbol for what?

⑪ What is Switzerland's largest city?

⑫ For what crime was Al Capone convicted in 1931?

⑬ What is a *koto*?

⑭ Which former Nazi headed the US missile programme?

⑮ What do the initials stand for in rugby legend J P R Williams?

⑯ Who was Inspector Tom Barnaby's first sergeant?

QUIZ 25

1. What is the national language of Pakistan?

2. In which novel is Edmond Dantès a prisoner?

3. What is a gibbous moon?

4. Who partnered Kara Tointon to victory in the 2010 *Strictly*?

5. In which English city was King Edgar crowned in 973?

6. Which novelist won the 2011 Booker Prize?

7. What name is given to a Scottish peak over 914m (3000ft)?

8. Who did John Hinckley Jr take a shot at in 1981?

9. Which song begins: 'The old home town looks the same . . .'?

10. Where is the Prado museum?

11. Which US president's home was Mount Vernon?

12. Which two countries share the Douro River?

13. Where did Molly Malone live?

14. The star Cirius is also known as what?

15. Who wrote twelve volumes about Casanova?

16. Which showbiz surname do Jake and Maggie share?

QUIZ 26

① Who was Led Zeppelin's lead singer?

② In which country are the King Leopold Ranges?

③ What, in Spain, is *El Gordo*?

④ Who is the patron saint of bankers?

⑤ In which branch of science was Alfred Adler influential?

⑥ Who was known as the 'Bouncing Czech'?

⑦ What is the name of Monaco's ruling family?

⑧ Which writer started life as Daniel Foe?

⑨ What is children's TV character Bob the Builder's catchphrase?

⑩ Who succeeded Lord Carrington as UK foreign secretary in 1982?

⑪ Who composed *The Damnation of Faust*?

⑫ What is Argentina's currency?

⑬ Which cricketer hit six sixes in a single over in 1985?

⑭ In which country did speed skating originate?

⑮ What does OXFAM stand for?

⑯ What castle is the family seat of the Dukes of Norfolk?

QUIZ 27

① What is the title of Barack Obama's 2010 children's book?

② Mt Everest stands in which two countries?

③ Whose first address was 155 Norman Rd, Leytonstone, London?

④ What is the sixth Commandment?

⑤ Who wrote *The Aeneid*?

⑥ Who was the first narrator of *Thomas the Tank Engine* on TV?

⑦ What does Buenos Aires mean?

⑧ AMSTRAD stands for what?

⑨ Where on a ship is the gunwale?

⑩ What is the French word for scallop?

⑪ Who was The Yardbirds' lead singer?

⑫ What is the name of Conan Doyle's 'lost world'?

⑬ Which famous sea battle took place on 31 May 1916?

⑭ Cinnamon and Silver Fox are breeds of which animal?

⑮ ET on a car number plate indicates which country of origin?

⑯ Which French director was in *Close Encounters of the Third Kind*?

QUIZ 28

① How many Crusades were there?

② What was George Eliot's last novel?

③ How many pounds are there in 10 kilograms?

④ Which Israeli couple had a No 1 hit in the UK in 1968?

⑤ Which US boxing world champion's real name was Walker Smith?

⑥ Which English monarch was 'the wisest fool in Christendom'?

⑦ Hg is the symbol for which chemical element?

⑧ *Chemin de fer* is French for what?

⑨ Who recited one of his poems at President Kennedy's inauguration?

⑩ Which English cathedral has the tallest spire?

⑪ Do cats and dogs have a bellybutton?

⑫ How many witches are there in *Macbeth*?

⑬ Who painted the *Girl with a Pearl Earring*?

⑭ Who was the first prime minister to live at 10 Downing Street?

⑮ What is an exploding star called?

⑯ Who played Louise in the film *Thelma and Louise*?

QUIZ 29

1. Which two US states border Florida?

2. What must Caesar's wife be above?

3. Which fictional detective lives in Whitehaven Mansions?

4. What does 'bovine' mean?

5. What means of transport did Icarus use?

6. Who composed the opera *The Flying Dutchman*?

7. Who painted *The Garden of Earthly Delights*?

8. Which military duke's home was known as 'Number One, London'?

9. Which amphibian sang with Kylie Minogue on her show in 2001?

10. How does a digitigrade animal walk?

11. Which schoolboy is said to have invented the sport of rugby?

12. Who won the 2011 Formula One British Grand Prix?

13. What did the singer Marie Lawrie change her name to?

14. In which make of car was James Dean killed?

15. What do Americans call a caravan site?

16. Name the only bird with nostrils at the tip of its beak.

QUIZ 30

① Which is the older club, Manchester City or Manchester United?

② What colour bonnet did supporters of the French Revolution wear?

③ Which is larger, North or South Dakota?

④ Which English city is Engelbert Humperdinck from?

⑤ In which of her homes did Queen Victoria die?

⑥ What has Britain become in George Orwell's *1984*?

⑦ What was Mafia boss Albert Anastasia doing when he was murdered?

⑧ Which ex-Beatle recorded 'Wonderful Christmastime'?

⑨ What is the ridge between the shoulder blades of a horse called?

⑩ What is the country retreat of US presidents?

⑪ Whose residence is the Apostolic Palace?

⑫ What is the Indian name for Calcutta?

⑬ Who were known in the gossip columns as 'Ken and Em'?

⑭ What does the musical term *allegro* mean?

⑮ What is 'the thief of time'?

⑯ What is the principal island of the Inner Hebrides?

QUIZ 31
MUSIC

① Which 1980s band's name means 'fast fashion'?

② Where was singer Justin Bieber discovered?

③ Who was the UK *X Factor*'s first female judge?

④ Twiggy had her only hit with which song?

⑤ Which Aussie singer's grandad won the Nobel Prize for Physics?

⑥ In which year did television's *Top of the Pops* come to an end?

⑦ Who are the 'Duke', the 'Earl' and the 'Count'?

⑧ How is Mendelssohn's *Overture to the Hebrides* also known?

⑨ Who composed the music for *Million Dollar Baby*?

⑩ How old was Jools Holland when he formed Squeeze?

⑪ Who wrote the lyrics for the 1996 hit 'Three Lions'?

⑫ Which country won the 2010 Eurovision Song Contest?

⑬ Who was the first female singer to have ten No 1 UK singles?

⑭ In his early days what was Stevie Wonder known as?

⑮ Who composed 'The Dambusters March'?

⑯ What is the colour if 'Football is the Game'?

QUIZ 32

① In which country is the mountain K2?

② Which three letters in the alphabet have no straight lines?

③ What whale excretion is used in the making of perfume?

④ Which perfume house created Fahrenheit?

⑤ Name the author of *Uncle Tom's Cabin*.

⑥ Who played Juan Perón in the 1996 film *Evita*?

⑦ Is a cat's body temperature higher or lower than a human's?

⑧ On which continent is Graham Land?

⑨ Who gave thanks for 'the Aintree Iron'?

⑩ In *Harry Potter*, where does Professor Severus Snape live?

⑪ Which stand-up comic is a descendant of William Thackeray?

⑫ What does EMS stand for?

⑬ How many faces has an icosidodecahedron?

⑭ What is the correct way to address a duke?

⑮ Which artist painted *The Night Watch*?

⑯ In which country was composer Irving Berlin born?

QUIZ 33

① Angelina Jolie's first child was adopted in which country?

② What did the superstitious Bjorn Borg not do during Wimbledon?

③ Which European country has some 187,000 lakes?

④ What word describes someone who puts pleasure above all else?

⑤ Battledore was an early form of which sport?

⑥ Which TV actor sang in character for his hit 'Grandad'?

⑦ Ile de France is a common breed of which farm animal?

⑧ What does OT stand for?

⑨ Why were sailors called 'jack tars'?

⑩ In which film did Mickey Mouse make his screen debut?

⑪ How was the 1st Earl of Stockton formerly known?

⑫ Which 17th-century English poet was Dean of St Paul's Cathedral?

⑬ In which London pub did Ronnie Kray commit murder?

⑭ Which Beatle was once a messenger for British Railways?

⑮ What was Lenin's profession before becoming a revolutionary?

⑯ John Steinbeck's *East of Eden* is based on which biblical story?

QUIZ 34

1. What do the Americans call spring onions?

2. Who was the US actor behind the rebuilding of the Globe Theatre?

3. Which perennial weed can be 'woolly' or 'cotton'?

4. The source of the River Thames is in which county?

5. Which famous racehorse was kidnapped in 1983?

6. What was the name of the motel in *Psycho*?

7. How many syllables are there in a haiku?

8. What does the Chinese word *chow* mean?

9. Chatsworth is the stately home of which ducal family?

10. Which Scottish singer used to work in a frozen fish factory?

11. Where is the poet William Wordsworth buried?

12. In which year did George V come to the throne?

13. Which Mahler symphony is known as the 'Resurrection'?

14. In which US city was crime writer Raymond Chandler born?

15. Which Lou was vocalist with Velvet Underground?

16. Which everyday item did Alessandro Volta help develop?

QUIZ 35

① In which city is South Africa's parliament?

② Which item of headgear takes its name from a 19th-century battle?

③ Who became leader of the Conservative Party in September 2001?

④ How many countries are there in the British Commonwealth?

⑤ If you are gamophobic what are you afraid of?

⑥ Who was England's first Test cricket captain?

⑦ What is epistaxis?

⑧ Which popular US singer died in 2007, aged 93?

⑨ Which 1960s England cricket captain was a double international?

⑩ Which playwright was a convicted member of the IRA?

⑪ Hanoi is located on the right bank of which river?

⑫ A medieval knight in search of adventure was called a what?

⑬ Which has the most toes, an emu or an ostrich?

⑭ Which presidential wife was known as the 'Iron Butterfly'?

⑮ What is 'Just William's' surname?

⑯ What was the UEFA Cup formerly called?

QUIZ 36

1. How many red cards are there in a standard pack?

2. Who was the first man to reach the South Pole?

3. Which Norse goddess's chariot was pulled by cats?

4. In which city is the football club Juventus based?

5. San José is the capital of which country?

6. In which film does John Wayne play the role of Davy Crockett?

7. What do the presidential initials FDR stand for?

8. In which ocean was the deserted *Marie Celeste* found in 1872?

9. What is the Zodiac sign for Capricorn?

10. Who wrote the play *Doctor Faustus*?

11. Which UK prime minister's wife was a published poet?

12. What do you study in a formicarium?

13. What is Scotland's most north-westerly point?

14. Which cricketer was known as the 'Master Blaster'?

15. Which two fish go into a salade niçoise?

16. Which star raised £10 million for Darfur?

QUIZ 37

① What monumental work of art did France gift to the USA in 1886?

② Which composer was born in Salzburg in 1756?

③ Jeremy Irons was a presenter on which children's TV show?

④ Who became head of the International Monetary Fund in 2011?

⑤ What is the official residence of the French President?

⑥ In Greek mythology, which dog had three heads?

⑦ On what river does St Petersburg stand?

⑧ Whose dog killed one of the Queen's corgis in 2003?

⑨ Who is the patron saint of television?

⑩ In which sport might you experience an Eskimo roll?

⑪ Whose autobiography was entitled *The Coal Miner's Daughter*?

⑫ Which former member of The Who died in 2002?

⑬ What do the Americans call a flick knife?

⑭ Which world leader went into a coma in January 2006?

⑮ What is balsamic vinegar made from?

⑯ What was the former name of Malawi?

QUIZ 38
HISTORY

① Which war ended with the Treaty of Panmunjom?

② Who famously asked: 'Is Paris burning?'

③ Which country became part of Great Britain in 1801?

④ What did George Shillibeer introduce to London in 1829?

⑤ In which year was 19 October 'Black Monday'?

⑥ Who was the US president at the outbreak of World War One?

⑦ Which English king was crowned twice?

⑧ Who was the Dutch queen who died in 2004?

⑨ When was the Bay of Pigs invasion of Cuba?

⑩ Who was the South African prime minister assassinated in 1966?

⑪ Who was the first woman to fly the Atlantic solo?

⑫ Which English king was deemed to be 'unready'?

⑬ Prince George of Denmark was married to which English queen?

⑭ Which 1957 treaty established the European Economic Community?

⑮ Which British royal dynasty began in 1714?

⑯ What did George V give up for World War One?

QUIZ 39

① Which royal couple was divorced in 1996?

② What are the colours of the Polish flag?

③ What was Thomas Paine's 18th-century ground-breaking book?

④ Parkesine was the first man-made what?

⑤ What are the protective leather trousers worn by cowboys?

⑥ The writer Gabriel García Márquez is a native of which country?

⑦ Which US general did Gregory Peck portray in a 1977 film?

⑧ In what country was Zoroastrianism founded?

⑨ Who was Robert De Niro's first wife?

⑩ Diamond is the birthstone for which month?

⑪ What is the emblem of the New Zealand All Blacks?

⑫ Who was nicknamed 'Lord Porn'?

⑬ To which country do the Faroe Islands belong?

⑭ Who composed the music for the film *Lawrence of Arabia*?

⑮ In which year was Coca Cola invented: 1886, 1896, 1906?

⑯ What is the collective noun for trout?

QUIZ 40

① What gas is produced during a thunderstorm?

② Which film star's daughter killed gangster Johnny Stompanato?

③ Who directed the 2009 film *Public Enemies*?

④ Which country did Russia invade in 1956?

⑤ Rarotonga is the capital of which group of islands?

⑥ What friendly alliance did Britain and France sign in 1904?

⑦ Which country put six goals past England at Wembley in 1953?

⑧ In Greek mythology, who was the boatman on the River Styx?

⑨ Which of T S Eliot's poetical cats is called the Hidden Paw?

⑩ How many hours are there in a week?

⑪ Which role did Phil Collins play on stage in *Oliver*?

⑫ Mulefoot and red wattle are breeds of what animal?

⑬ In which comic novel is Charles Pooter the central character?

⑭ How many provinces does Canada have?

⑮ Who was on the cover of the first issue of *Playboy* magazine?

⑯ What is endocrinology?

QUIZ 41

① What kind of bridge is the Forth Rail Bridge?

② Who in 2010 became Australia's first female prime minister?

③ Ginny Leng was a world champion in which sport?

④ What do the letters of Dr Who's TARDIS stand for?

⑤ In music, what is a scale performed at great speed called?

⑥ What is the hottest of the planets?

⑦ In the Robin Williams film, what is Mrs Doubtfire's first name?

⑧ Who was the lead singer in Procol Harum?

⑨ What does CBE stand for?

⑩ In which Spanish city is the Alhambra palace?

⑪ What is the official language of Andorra?

⑫ Which cleric founded the *L'Académie française*?

⑬ 'Vaccination' comes from the Latin name for which animal?

⑭ Who wrote a regular newspaper column as the 'Wednesday Witch'?

⑮ Who said: 'Jaw-jaw is better than war-war.'

⑯ Whose 1998 hit was 'Viva Forever'?

QUIZ 42

① Which US state is due south of Colorado?

② Who said: 'As God once said, and I think rightly . . . '?

③ Who is the inventor of the DeLorean time machine?

④ How many players in a water polo team?

⑤ Who was Henry VIII's fifth wife?

⑥ A Sally Lunn is a type of what?

⑦ What is Italy's longest river?

⑧ Talipes is the medical term for which physical deformity?

⑨ Who wrote the novel *Rich Man, Poor Man*?

⑩ Which celebrated explorer became an MP in 1895?

⑪ Who composed the *Academic Festival Overture*?

⑫ Whose rhyming nickname at school was 'Bathing Towel'?

⑬ What is the world's hardest and heaviest wood?

⑭ In which year did the New York City Subway open?

⑮ What does OED stand for?

⑯ Which old river just keeps 'rollin' along'?

QUIZ 43

① The FIDE is the governing body of which board game?

② Which country has the shortest coastline in the world?

③ Which famous English writer once clean bowled W G Grace?

④ What part of a plant produces pollen?

⑤ For which novel did Kingsley Amis win the Booker Prize?

⑥ Who succeeded Roy Plomley as host of *Desert Island Discs*?

⑦ Aluminium is made from which mineral?

⑧ Amongst singer-songwriters, who is 'The Boss'?

⑨ Who was Harold Wilson's long-serving secretary?

⑩ What is the name of the Hungarian paprika-flavoured stew?

⑪ The Whitsunday Islands are off the coast of which country?

⑫ Who was Clement Freud's on-screen canine companion?

⑬ How is the *Coccinella septempunctata* better known?

⑭ Which famous son went missing in the Sahara in 1982?

⑮ Which Mary is half of a twin acting duo?

⑯ Who wrote the title song for the film *Grease*?

QUIZ 44

① Thomas Hardy's novels are set in which fictional county?

② Which country has the minority share of Lake Geneva?

③ In which industry did Andrew Carnegie make his fortune?

④ The malleus, incus and stapes are bones in which body part?

⑤ In which century did Rococo art and architecture develop?

⑥ In which country is the Shwedagon or 'Golden' Pagoda?

⑦ Which Minister of Health introduced the NHS?

⑧ What are you afraid of if you are pogonophobic?

⑨ What is the US branch of the Mafia called?

⑩ Name the other half: Hero and . . .

⑪ Who won more Oscars, Bette Davis or Katherine Hepburn?

⑫ How high is the Burj Khalifa in Dubai (to the nearest 100m)?

⑬ From which fruit is cassis made?

⑭ Which Italian artist painted *The Birth of Venus*?

⑮ What does a deltiologist collect: fans or postcards?

⑯ Whose catchphrase was: 'All done in the best possible taste'?

QUIZ 45
GEOGRAPHY

1. In which Australian state is the town of Wagga Wagga?

2. Baku is the capital of which country?

3. What is the largest island in the Caribbean Sea?

4. In which famous square is St Basil's Cathedral?

5. Which two countries does the Simplon Tunnel link?

6. What is the windy region between latitudes 40° and 50°S called?

7. What is the largest country in Africa?

8. Which English port shares the name of Delaware's state capital?

9. Which desert is in southern Israel?

10. What language do Walloons traditionally speak?

11. Dong is the currency of which country?

12. Which Canadian airport is named after a former prime minister?

13. What was Gdańsk previously called?

14. Which sea is named after the seaweed that floats on its surface?

15. Which English city is 266 miles from London?

16. What is the largest city within the Arctic Circle?

QUIZ 46

① Who were the founders of Band Aid?

② How many time zones are there in the contiguous USA?

③ Whose catchphrase was: 'Up and under'?

④ A boomer is a male what?

⑤ Who was The War of Jenkin's Ear between?

⑥ Which of his ears did Vincent Van Gogh cut off?

⑦ Who wrote *The Portrait of a Lady*?

⑧ Which Canadian won Eurovision for Switzerland in 1988?

⑨ For which footballing nation did Eusebio play?

⑩ What does *magnus opus* mean?

⑪ What is the collective noun for bears?

⑫ What is a two-masted sailing ship with square sails?

⑬ Otto Lilienthal was a pioneer of which mode of travel?

⑭ What is the ship's surgeon's name in *Master and Commander*?

⑮ Whose ghost walks the battlements in Shakespeare's play *Hamlet*?

⑯ What does QANTAS stand for?

QUIZ 47

① Who first made a hit out of 'Walking In The Air'?

② What nationality is the writer Margaret Atwood?

③ What is the chemical in chillies that makes them hot?

④ Who is Ravi Shankar's singer daughter?

⑤ What did the shelling of Fort Sumter start?

⑥ Which former child star made her directorial debut with *Whip It*?

⑦ Who wrote the music for the hymn 'Onward Christian Soldiers'?

⑧ Who became scandalously known as DSK?

⑨ In which castle are Scotland's crown jewels kept?

⑩ What is the name of the Flintstones' home town?

⑪ In cycling, what is BMX short for?

⑫ What was the 2004 debut album of the Scissor Sisters called?

⑬ What is Billie Piper's middle name?

⑭ Which American poet was charged with treason in 1945?

⑮ Who became Archbishop of Canterbury in 1980?

⑯ What is the collective noun for weasels?

QUIZ 48

① Who wrote the poem 'Suicide in the Trenches'?

② What is the longest bone in the body?

③ Which country won most medals at the 2008 Olympics?

④ Who was Frank Sinatra's last wife?

⑤ Who said: 'All I know is that I am not a Marxist.'

⑥ Who bought the Lennon & McCartney songbook in 1985?

⑦ What does OPEC stand for?

⑧ How many prongs are there on a tuning fork?

⑨ Which *New Tricks* co-stars are married to each other in real life?

⑩ What is a peccary?

⑪ Richard Hannay is the hero in a series of novels by whom?

⑫ What was Buffalo Bill's real name?

⑬ Which is the most easterly city in England?

⑭ How many nerve cells does the brain have, 100 million or 100 billion?

⑮ *Glass of Absinthe* is a sculpture by which 20th-century artist?

⑯ Which is England's third oldest university?

QUIZ 49

① What does ECG stand for?

② To which country do the Azores belong?

③ Who led the Peasants' Revolt of 1381?

④ Are bats blind?

⑤ Who was America's first First Lady?

⑥ Which London Underground line is older, Bakerloo or Central?

⑦ The River Tamar is in which Australian state?

⑧ Loch Ness, Long Bow and Sprite are varieties of what?

⑨ What is a female foal called?

⑩ Which star of the film *Genevieve* died in 1959?

⑪ Which famous cat was created by Otto Messmer?

⑫ In which sport was Molly Hide an England star performer?

⑬ Who was The Drifters' lead singer?

⑭ Who was the greatest female poet of the ancient world?

⑮ Which shipping forecast area is further north, Rockall or Bailey?

⑯ What is slang for an Eton jacket?

QUIZ 50

① What is the port of Athens?

② Who is Bolivia named after?

③ In the world of pop, who did Thomas Woodward become?

④ What is a baby cockroach called?

⑤ What is France's top literary prize?

⑥ For how many years was Robinson Crusoe marooned?

⑦ What does RIBA stand for?

⑧ Name the BBC reporter captured in Gaza in 2007.

⑨ What is the largest country in the world?

⑩ Which French wine region produces Sancerre?

⑪ Which soul singer performed at President Obama's inauguration?

⑫ Which US novelist wrote *The Crying of Lot 49*?

⑬ What is another name for a microchip?

⑭ Which jazz quartet got into the charts with 'Take Five'?

⑮ Who designed the Morris Minor?

⑯ How many feet are there in a mile and a half?

QUIZ 51

① Who composed the *March Slav*?

② What item of headgear did Ecuador give to the world?

③ The devil's coach-horse is what type of insect?

④ What is the chemical symbol for gold?

⑤ Who was only 12 when she sang in the 1976 Royal Variety Show?

⑥ The Mississippi and Missouri meet near which US city?

⑦ Who is Scrooge's deceased partner in *A Christmas Carol*?

⑧ How many biblical plagues of Egypt were there?

⑨ In Morse code, what letter is represented by four dots?

⑩ How many permanent members of the UN Security Council are there?

⑪ On whose play is Rossini's opera *William Tell* based?

⑫ Which city is 36 miles west of Manchester?

⑬ The American crime series *The Wire* is set in which city?

⑭ Who directed the film *Halloween*?

⑮ Who is the patron saint of travellers?

⑯ In the song 'Waltzing Matilda', what is a matilda?

QUIZ 52
SPORT

① Graham Swann made his Test debut against which country?

② How many yellow cards appeared in the 2010 FIFA World Cup Final?

③ Which country made its Rugby World Cup debut in 2011?

④ What is the maximum weight of a golf ball?

⑤ What non-clothes item are jockeys not allowed to wear?

⑥ 'Brain fade' is motor-racing slang for what?

⑦ Which athlete was known as 'The Flying Housewife'?

⑧ Who get to lift the Vince Lombardi Trophy?

⑨ Which rugby league player was nicknamed 'Chariots'?

⑩ Who became President of the MCC in 2010?

⑪ Who resigned as Celtic manager in May 2009?

⑫ Who was the US Ryder Cup captain in 2010?

⑬ In snooker, which colour ball is worth six points?

⑭ How many events are in a heptathlon?

⑮ What nationality is racing driver Rubens Barrichello?

⑯ What is the only Test cricket ground below sea level?

QUIZ 53

1. Who did George Michael break up with in 1986?

2. What kind of computer file is a bitmap?

3. Which two symbols are featured on Turkey's national flag?

4. What is the covering of a deer's antler called?

5. Whose piano music accompanied *The Sting*?

6. Which Latin legal term means 'at first sight'?

7. Split Waterman captained England in what sport?

8. Where in London is Poets' Corner?

9. What do the initials stand for in P G Wodehouse?

10. Who was stripped of his knighthood for spying?

11. Which is further north, Adelaide or Canberra?

12. Who are Huey, Dewey and Louie?

13. In which year was the first Tour de France staged?

14. Who replaced Charlie Sheen in *Two and a Half Men*?

15. Which European country has the oldest parliament?

16. And what is it called?

QUIZ 54

① On which day of the week did Solomon Grundy marry?

② Who wrote the *Pink Panther* theme?

③ What year was the Lockerbie air disaster?

④ What is the capital of Taiwan?

⑤ Who created a plan for Europe after World War Two?

⑥ Clarice Cliff is best known as a designer of what?

⑦ Which member of the royal family is a qualified architect?

⑧ In Hawaiian, does *aloha* mean hello or goodbye?

⑨ The moons of Uranus are named after characters from whose plays?

⑩ Who directed the award-winning film *Pan's Labyrinth*?

⑪ Which TV presenter was Nick Clegg's fag at school?

⑫ Whose last words were: 'Let's cool it, brothers'?

⑬ Which weapon did H G Wells anticipate in a 1903 story?

⑭ Who were the song and dance duo of the stage show *Viva la Diva*?

⑮ What kitchen 'instrument' is used for slicing vegetables?

⑯ What is usually kept in a bandbox?

QUIZ 55

① What is QUANGO short for?

② What type of gun was the German 'Big Bertha'?

③ Who was Abraham Lincoln's assassin?

④ With what name did Bruce Forsyth start out in life?

⑤ Which US state borders just one other US state?

⑥ Which 1970s pop group regrouped for the 2007 Grammys?

⑦ In which year did Durham become a first-class cricket county?

⑧ What is another term for Chinese white cabbage?

⑨ The port of Arkhangelsk has access to which sea?

⑩ What was the former capital of Yemen?

⑪ How was Ilich Ramírez Sánchez better known?

⑫ What did Charles Perrault collect?

⑬ What is Spider-Man's real name?

⑭ Which letter is to the right of B on a computer keyboard?

⑮ What is Inspector Maigret's first name?

⑯ How was the South African town of Centurion formerly known?

QUIZ 56

1. What was Mozart's middle name?

2. Malta comprises what three inhabited islands?

3. Who was the creator of *Thomas the Tank Engine*?

4. What does ESSO stand for?

5. Which former jazz pianist became principal conductor of the LSO?

6. For which film did Jeff Bridges win an Oscar in 2010?

7. In Greek mythology, who stole some of Apollo's cattle?

8. Gordon Brown gained a 'first' in which subject at university?

9. Who was Britain's first woman astronaut?

10. Who is older, Vic Reeves or Bob Mortimer?

11. In which hemisphere is the Tropic of Cancer?

12. Whose book *Tropic of Cancer* was banned for many years?

13. In what year was the BBC founded: 1922, 1924 or 1926?

14. Whose 2003 debut album was *Twentysomething*?

15. How many countries border France?

16. What is *pâté de foie gras*?

QUIZ 57

(1) Who was US president at the end of World War Two?

(2) The poet C Day Lewis wrote thrillers under which pseudonym?

(3) What is Gary's surname in *Men Behaving Badly*?

(4) Who said: 'Your president is no crook'?

(5) What links the Celtic Sea to the Irish Sea?

(6) What is the name of the Rugby World Cup trophy?

(7) What is Inspector Morse's first name?

(8) Which is the third book in the *Harry Potter* series?

(9) In the Bible, who first saw the writing on the wall?

(10) Which 007's father was a policeman?

(11) When was the Watergate break-in: 1968, 1972 or 1975?

(12) What does the herb borage taste like?

(13) In which play is Madame Arcati a character?

(14) What is pinchbeck?

(15) Which British tree has berries sometimes called 'snotty gogs'?

(16) What is one third of one half?

QUIZ 58

1. How many national flags does Scotland have?

2. Suffolk Bang is a variety of what foodstuff?

3. Who is known as the first 'Queen of Gospel Music'?

4. What was Chennai previously named?

5. Who was Destiny's Child's lead singer?

6. What nationality was French queen Marie Antoinette?

7. Which is larger, North or South Carolina?

8. Which country has the golden wattle as its national flower?

9. Who is the hero of the novel *Lorna Doone*?

10. What animal does a *mahout* take care of?

11. Which Brown was British foreign secretary in the 1960s?

12. Which parts of the Venus de Milo's body are missing?

13. Who was the first British monarch to abdicate?

14. Which fruit has more calories than any other?

15. How many strings does a balalaika have?

16. In which country was designer Yves Saint-Laurent born?

QUIZ 59
CINEMA & TV

① In which Bond film did Rowan Atkinson make his big screen debut?

② The TV drama series *Mad Men* is centred around which profession?

③ Who does Michael J Fox play in the *Back to the Future* films?

④ Which TV cook was at home at No 11 Downing Street?

⑤ Who did James Lablanche Stewart become on the big screen?

⑥ *Inspector George Gently* is filmed in which overseas city?

⑦ Who does John Hurt play in *Tinker Tailor Soldier Spy*?

⑧ Which organization presents the Golden Globe Awards?

⑨ *The Left Handed Gun* is about which outlaw?

⑩ In *Boardwalk Empire*, what is 'Nucky' Thompson's job?

⑪ Cecily and Gwendolyn were what in *The Odd Couple*?

⑫ Who plays Carson in *Downton Abbey*?

⑬ Name the other half: Simon Pegg and . . .

⑭ Who was the eldest Marx Brother: Chico, Groucho or Harpo?

⑮ In which Seattle apartment block does Dr Frasier Crane live?

⑯ Name the female character played by Dustin Hoffman in *Tootsie*.

QUIZ 60

① Where in Italy was Leonardo da Vinci born?

② What is the largest seed in the plant kingdom?

③ Is the Chinook wind of the Rocky Mountains warm or cold?

④ Which Milan fashion house began with a Sicilian and a Venetian?

⑤ Who was the first king of Israel?

⑥ To which actress was Sting first married?

⑦ In *The Archers*, who fatally fell off a roof?

⑧ Who made jewelled Easter eggs for the Russian royal family?

⑨ How many pins are used in skittles?

⑩ What is the county town of Wiltshire?

⑪ In the financial world, what does NASDAQ stand for?

⑫ *The Agony and the Ecstasy* movie was about which artist?

⑬ Which tradesman would use a quern?

⑭ What did J B Priestley describe as 'London's broadest street'?

⑮ Which bridge is nicknamed 'The Coathanger'?

⑯ What was the only US group to appear on the 'Do They Know It's Christmas?' single?

QUIZ 61

① Who is Sherlock Holmes' housekeeper?

② Who was prime minister at the time of Edward VIII's abdication?

③ Which jockey was badly hurt at Aintree on Grand National Day 2011?

④ How many verses does the English National Anthem have?

⑤ What is fine sediment deposited by a river called?

⑥ What is known as the 'King of the Spey'?

⑦ Which household item is made from naphthalene?

⑧ Who was the second president of the USA?

⑨ What animal did the Russians send into space in 1957?

⑩ Which George was engaged to Linda Ronstadt?

⑪ What is Prince Harry's full name?

⑫ What fungus is used in the production of alcohol?

⑬ In which US state is Dodge City?

⑭ What is the most common non-contagious disease?

⑮ Where were the Bee Gees born?

⑯ Which country is between Algeria and Libya?

QUIZ 62

① What does NASA stand for?

② Who was the last monarch of the House of Stuart?

③ Which is the southernmost city in England?

④ What is the oldest university in Paris?

⑤ What was Camilla Parker Bowles' maiden name?

⑥ Where do peanut pods ripen?

⑦ What was Indonesia previously known as?

⑧ How many letters are there in the modern Welsh alphabet?

⑨ What is the international dialling code for Spain?

⑩ Which instrument did Lionel Hampton play?

⑪ Who was the first prime minister of Israel?

⑫ Which composer's last word was 'Mozart!'?

⑬ What is the largest star on the Australian flag called?

⑭ What plant devours insects?

⑮ Who was Peeping Tom peeping at?

⑯ For what did Annie Lennox win an Oscar in 2004?

QUIZ 63

① How is Declan Patrick MacManus better known?

② Who killed Lee Harvey Oswald?

③ In which country was the European business school INSEAD founded?

④ Who sang 'Something Stupid' with Robbie Williams?

⑤ What is dendrology?

⑥ Which former England cricketer's initials are MCC?

⑦ Where in Australia are the MacDonnell Ranges?

⑧ Californian, yellow horned and opium are types of what?

⑨ Who was the first black US secretary of state?

⑩ Which serial killer lived at 10 Rillington Place?

⑪ Who wrote *A Portrait of the Artist as a Young Man*?

⑫ Which UK island's flag features three conjoined legs?

⑬ What nationality was the singing duo Nina and Frederick?

⑭ Which is the only male creature to give birth?

⑮ What trees can grow above the tree line?

⑯ Which serial killer did Dominic West portray in a 2011 TV drama?

QUIZ 64

(1) Who directed the 1996 film *The English Patient*?

(2) Whose novel humorously observed that *Aunts Aren't Gentlemen*?

(3) Who did Nicholas Sarkozy succeed as president of France?

(4) What was Harold Wilson's favourite holiday destination?

(5) Which nation first gave women the right to vote?

(6) What was London's first one-way street?

(7) In which decade was the Frisbee invented?

(8) Which Alexandre Dumas was the novelist – father or son?

(9) How old was Michael Hutchence when he died?

(10) What was Robbie Williams' job before joining Take That?

(11) Into which sea does the Mekong River flow?

(12) Which former agony aunt died in 2010?

(13) Samuel Cooper is famous for what type of 17th-century painting?

(14) What did Jerry's Guide to the World Wide Web become?

(15) Ben Lomond and Baldwin are types of which fruit?

(16) How many days will the year 2100 contain?

QUIZ 65

1. Whose assassination in Sarajevo in 1914 led to World War One?

2. On which geological fault line is San Francisco?

3. Which Hemingway book title comes from a line by John Donne?

4. How is Joseph Aloisius Ratzinger better known?

5. Which elderly magazine was founded in 1992?

6. On which sea is the port of Odessa?

7. What do Italians call seafood fried in batter?

8. What was Olivia Newton-John's song for Eurovision 1974?

9. Who does Derek Jacobi play in *The King's Speech*?

10. Which Chinese river is longer, Yangtze or Yellow?

11. Which museum is home to the *Mona Lisa*?

12. How did soul singer Sam Cooke die?

13. Who told the British public: 'You've never had it so good'?

14. Who wrote *The Vicar of Wakefield*?

15. Which playwright became his country's president in 1989?

16. What was Manchester United originally called?

QUIZ 66

1. What branch of the armed services did Pam Ayres join?

2. Where did Rick Stein open his first restaurant outside Padstow?

3. What is the capital of Yemen?

4. Who said: 'Publish and be damned!'?

5. How many stars are there on the Chinese national flag?

6. Which, in 1878, became the first university to admit women?

7. Whose first of many books was called *Jigsaw*?

8. Name the winged horse in Greek mythology.

9. Who is the patron saint of Glasgow?

10. Which ex-wife of a president was sentenced to jail in 2003?

11. Who was lead singer of Black Sabbath?

12. Who scored a century on his England Test debut in 1993?

13. Where did Alexander the Great die?

14. Who was Cleo Laine's bandleader husband?

15. Where in India is the Taj Mahal?

16. What is Miss Piggy's surname?

QUIZ 67
SCIENCE & NATURE

① What gas is the most dense?

② Dry ice is a solid form of what?

③ What is the chemical symbol for potassium?

④ Which bear is bigger: brown, grizzly or polar?

⑤ What is the world's most poisonous spider?

⑥ Amber is a type of what?

⑦ What is surgically removed in a brachiotomy?

⑧ The Earth's inner core mainly consists of what?

⑨ Which Australian animal's name means 'no drink'?

⑩ How many eyelids does a camel have?

⑪ Which scientist devised the three laws of motion?

⑫ What is the area of seabed closest to land called?

⑬ What is AIDS short for?

⑭ Which animal can be red, arctic or bat-eared?

⑮ Which is the only bird that can fly backwards?

⑯ Who is the author of *The Selfish Gene*?

QUIZ 68

① Who was George Gershwin's lyricist brother?

② Which royal princess wrote *The Serpent and the Moon*?

③ On which group of islands is Scapa?

④ The Ukrainian city of Kiev stands on which river?

⑤ What is the official country home of the British prime minister?

⑥ What camera did George Eastman launch in 1888?

⑦ What was writer Joseph Conrad's first language?

⑧ Which English artist is famous for Op Art?

⑨ What relation is journalist Emma Freud to Sigmund Freud?

⑩ What is dactylology?

⑪ Which racecourse is home to the St Leger?

⑫ On which part of an aircraft are the ailerons?

⑬ Which Jamaican singer starred in the film *The Harder They Come*?

⑭ Who was prime minister at the time of the Queen's Silver Jubilee?

⑮ Who was John the Baptist's father?

⑯ What musical instruments comprise a pair of dried Cuban gourds with beans inside?

QUIZ 69

1. Which motorway links Edinburgh and Glasgow?

2. Who played General Omar Bradley in the film *Patton*?

3. What is the county town of Shropshire?

4. Who was prime minister when Queen Victoria ascended the throne?

5. What did Henry Deringer invent in 1825?

6. In which country was the artist Francis Bacon born?

7. Which language has most native speakers, Bengali or Punjabi?

8. Who is Pip's benefactor in *Great Expectations*?

9. Which company created the first newsreel?

10. Which English king had the nickname 'Tum-Tum'?

11. Which girl's name means 'my father rejoices'?

12. Who was the manager of the Sex Pistols?

13. What is the collective noun for kangaroos?

14. If your birthday is 27 May, what is your star sign?

15. What were Kleenex tissues first intended for?

16. Which English town is associated with the poet Philip Larkin?

QUIZ 70

① Who wrote the play *An Inspector Calls*?

② Who became US vice-president in 2009?

③ What is singer Susan Boyle's middle name?

④ Which *Only Fools and Horses* actor died in 2011 at 50?

⑤ Which two French words gave Velcro its name?

⑥ Who had a 1980s hit with 'Stand And Deliver'?

⑦ Who was the first man to hit a golf ball on the moon?

⑧ What does PVC stand for?

⑨ Which French actor starred in the 1966 film *Grand Prix*?

⑩ Which epic poem comes first, the *Iliad* or the *Odyssey*?

⑪ What safety feature appeared on London streets in 1925?

⑫ What is the county town of Devon?

⑬ Which oil company was founded by John D Rockefeller?

⑭ Whose last words were: 'Do not let poor Nelly starve'?

⑮ In which city were the 1920 Olympic Games held?

⑯ What was the Model T Ford car nicknamed?

QUIZ 71

① Which Barker wrote the 'Regeneration' trilogy?

② What is etymology?

③ What is the Jewish Day of Atonement also called?

④ Which movie star was one of the USA's most decorated soldiers?

⑤ In 1845 Alexander Cartwright wrote the rules for which game?

⑥ What became free on the streets of London in 2009?

⑦ How many substitutes are allowed in a rugby union game?

⑧ Which awful child did Francesca Simon give birth to?

⑨ What colour was Dyson's first bagless vacuum cleaner?

⑩ Who gave his name to his waterproof coat?

⑪ Who played Max Bialystock in the original film *The Producers*?

⑫ In which country were venetian blinds invented?

⑬ Which US crime writer worked for the Pinkerton Detective Agency?

⑭ Who is the most famous of the monstrous Gorgon sisters?

⑮ What does USSR stand for?

⑯ Complete the beer slogan: 'What We Want is . . .'

QUIZ 72

① *Wolf Hall* won who the 2009 Booker Prize?

② With which band did Angus Deayton have a hit single in 1980?

③ The mythological centaur is part man and part what?

④ Which sporting 'annual' was first published in 1864?

⑤ Which US president's wife was named Rosalynn?

⑥ Who in 2003 ran 7 marathons on 7 continents in 7 days?

⑦ In *Peter Pan*, what are the names of Wendy's brothers?

⑧ How is the artist Tiziano Vecelli better known?

⑨ What does 'gin' mean in cotton gin?

⑩ If you are crapulous what are you?

⑪ What does cwt stand for?

⑫ Which musical duo were Bill Medley and Bobby Hatfield?

⑬ Who are known as the 'Socceroos'?

⑭ Andrew Marr was formerly editor of which national newspaper?

⑮ What is Rupert Murdoch's first name?

⑯ Who said: 'There's a sucker born every minute'?

QUIZ 73

① Whose ad slogan was: 'A Little Dab'll Do Ya'?

② What was the name of Paul McCartney's first classical album?

③ In which London palace was Queen Elizabeth I born?

④ Demy and Royal are sizes of what?

⑤ What was the first British television channel to show colour?

⑥ Who was the first foreign secretary in the New Labour government?

⑦ Which tower was erected first, Blackpool or Eiffel?

⑧ Which football league club ground is in two countries?

⑨ What is examined using an otoscope?

⑩ The play *Romeo and Juliet* is mainly set in which Italian city?

⑪ From which musical does the song 'Sweet Transvestite' come?

⑫ In which country was lino invented?

⑬ Whose 12-novel series is *A Dance to the Music of Time*?

⑭ Which French daily newspaper was founded in 1828?

⑮ Which is the highest peak in England?

⑯ How many stars are on the flag of the European Union?

QUIZ 74
MUSIC

① What 2001 Bon Jovi hit was originally called *Ma vie en plus*?

② What is the US singer-songwriter Mýa's full name?

③ Who was 2002 *American Idol* winner with 'A Moment Like This'?

④ What was the group Gerry and the Pacemakers originally called?

⑤ What pitch was Amy Winehouse's voice?

⑥ The BBC banned which 1980s hit by Frankie Goes to Hollywood?

⑦ What did Ronan O'Rahilly set afloat in 1964?

⑧ In what year did Elvis Presley die?

⑨ What do the POWs whistle in *The Bridge Over the River Kwai*?

⑩ Who died first, Gilbert or Sullivan?

⑪ How old was *Top of the Pops* in 1989?

⑫ Who is lead vocalist of The Pussycat Dolls?

⑬ Which conductor co-founded the West-Eastern Divan Orchestra?

⑭ On Elton John's 'Nikita' who provided the falsetto backing?

⑮ In which year did the Glastonbury Festival all begin?

⑯ Which opera takes its name from the man who wrote the stories?

QUIZ 75

① Who wrote the novel *White Teeth*?

② Charles II's wife Catherine came from which European country?

③ Who was the first to exit *Strictly Come Dancing* 2011?

④ Cornwall was a centre for mining what?

⑤ What does SONAR stand for?

⑥ Who is the younger Attenborough, David or Richard?

⑦ Which country always leads the Olympic procession?

⑧ What does the F stand for in F Scott Fitzgerald?

⑨ Which musical instrument is on the soundtrack of *The Third Man*?

⑩ How many pecks are there in a bushel?

⑪ Which country's currency is the dalasi?

⑫ What does 'mahatma', as in Mahatma Gandhi, mean?

⑬ Herpes zoster is the medical name for what?

⑭ As well as a writer, Anton Chekhov was also a what?

⑮ Which rugby coach was knighted in 2010?

⑯ What is the UK's largest artificial lake?

QUIZ 76

① Which English monarch was called the 'Sailor King'?

② Which music is the theme for the film *Brief Encounter*?

③ What is the county town of Hampshire?

④ Who wrote the play *Edward II*?

⑤ Which nation's flag features a white three-towered temple?

⑥ Where in Paris is the tomb of Napoleon?

⑦ What type of creature is a Painted Goby?

⑧ Who led Britain to war in 1991?

⑨ Where were the 2010 Winter Olympics staged?

⑩ What did the crocodile swallow in *Peter Pan*?

⑪ In the TV show, what does QI stand for?

⑫ Who was the first English actor to be knighted?

⑬ Who is the author of *Lark Rise to Candleford*?

⑭ How was the muscular Angelo Siciliano better known?

⑮ Who was the first Archbishop of Canterbury?

⑯ Col. Gaddafi had an obsession about which US secretary of state?

QUIZ 77

1. In which country was Peter Andre born?

2. Who ended his diary entries with 'And so to bed'?

3. What is the second largest island in the world?

4. Who did Frankie Howerd play in *Up Pompeii*?

5. What did Eire leave in 1949?

6. Which is the northernmost city in England?

7. Which English general became the first Duke of Marlborough?

8. In which year was the 70mph speed limit introduced in the UK?

9. How many hours are there in a fortnight?

10. Uluru is the aboriginal name for what?

11. What date is Battle of Britain Day?

12. What is larger, a jackdaw or a rook?

13. Who is *The Hobbit* referred to in the title?

14. Which English novelist's real name is Franklin Birkinshaw?

15. What is the name of Del Boy's local?

16. What is the collective name for cockroaches?

QUIZ 78

① What is the capital of Morocco?

② Who created the hit TV series *The Wire*?

③ What tree can be Holm, Turkey or Sessile?

④ Which sheriff killed Billy the Kid?

⑤ Which insect performs the Waggle Dance?

⑥ In which book will you find the 'Pan-Galactic Gargle Blaster'?

⑦ What is the last book of the Old Testament?

⑧ In French, what day follows *mardi*?

⑨ What nationality was the spy Mata Hari?

⑩ What is the largest sand dune in Europe?

⑪ Winnie the Pooh lives in which wood?

⑫ What is 3 cubed?

⑬ What was the greatest tank battle of World War Two?

⑭ John Dee was a royal astrologer in which century?

⑮ Which is longer, a nautical mile or a land mile?

⑯ Which 18th-century classic tale has characters called Yahoos?

QUIZ 79

① Which ex-footballer has an airport named after him?

② In which city is the Rijksmuseum?

③ Whose painting, *Irises,* sold for $49m at auction in 1987?

④ Who does Philip Glenister play in *Life on Mars*?

⑤ Which former agony aunt's son is a well-known food critic?

⑥ Who was US vice president under George W Bush?

⑦ What labour-saving device did Edwin Beard Budding invent in 1830?

⑧ In computer terminology, what does HTML stand for?

⑨ What is the study of insects called?

⑩ New Zealand's Whanganui river flows into which sea?

⑪ Who was sacked as Welsh rugby coach in 2007?

⑫ Which *American Idol* finalist won an Oscar for *Dreamgirls*?

⑬ Who was the creator of *Only Fools and Horses* who died in 2011?

⑭ Which English artist's first names are Joseph Mallord William?

⑮ Who was the first Hollywood star to sign up in World War Two?

⑯ What is a young hippopotamus called?

QUIZ 80

1. Who was the first-ever football international between?

2. Which TV characters live at Winterdown Farm?

3. Rickets is caused by a deficiency of which vitamin?

4. Who wrote: 'To err is human, to forgive divine'?

5. Powdered eggs are eggs that have been what?

6. Which bestselling US writer became a recluse in the 1950s?

7. Add the showbiz surname: Donnie and Mark . . .

8. With which MP was Antonia de Sancha scandalously linked?

9. Which of the cat family is the biggest by weight?

10. What town is nearest to Parkhurst prison?

11. From which prison did the spy George Blake escape in 1966?

12. In which part of the human body are the carpal bones?

13. What is the largest citrus fruit?

14. Who wrote the poem 'The Hunting of the Snark'?

15. Which England cricketer fetched £450,000 at the 2009 IPL auction?

16. What does a misogynist hate?

QUIZ 81

① Which English novelist invented the pillar-box?

② A 'slam dunk' is a manoeuvre in which sport?

③ Which country did Britain invade in 1956?

④ Which newspaper does superhero Clark Kent work for?

⑤ What size crew did the Gemini spacecraft have?

⑥ Sherry derives its name from which Spanish town?

⑦ Who wrote *The Descent of Man*?

⑧ Which new British 'royal' was born on 23 March 1990?

⑨ Which country was once known as Cathay?

⑩ What is the longest river in Northern Ireland?

⑪ What is an SRN?

⑫ Who was the first black secretary-general of the United Nations?

⑬ What is larger, Newfoundland or Madagascar?

⑭ What is the bird cry of the male bittern called?

⑮ How many tales are there in Chaucer's *Canterbury Tales*?

⑯ What record did Vijaypat Singhania set in a hot air balloon in 2005?

QUIZ 82
HISTORY

1. In which battle did the Sioux defeat General Custer?

2. Who was UK prime minister at the outbreak of World War One?

3. Who said: 'The ballot is stronger than the bullet'?

4. Which Gandhi was assassinated in 1991?

5. For how long was John Paul I the Pope?

6. What was the name of Hitler's bunker for the Eastern front?

7. Which British monarch was the last Emperor of India?

8. Which Russian revolutionary was assassinated in 1940?

9. Name the other infamous half: 'Burke and . . .'

10. Whose was the first face to appear on a postage stamp?

11. Which queen is said to have written the 'Casket Letters'?

12. Which country did Robert Burke and William Wills explore?

13. Who was called 'Old Blood and Guts' by his troops?

14. Which great ruler died in 323 BC

15. Who did George Bush defeat in the 1988 US election?

16. Which English monarch was reputedly murdered in Berkeley Castle in 1327?

QUIZ 83

① What is the largest castle in Wales?

② From which plant does belladonna come?

③ How many times did Joe Frazier fight Muhammad Ali?

④ What is a *billet-doux*?

⑤ Lawrence Durrell's *Prospero's Cell* is about which Greek island?

⑥ What three countries border Luxembourg?

⑦ Which American playwright choked to death on a bottle cap in 1983?

⑧ What do the car initials MG stand for?

⑨ Which saint's day is on 25th October?

⑩ How many spires does Truro Cathedral have?

⑪ What does the word 'prolix' mean?

⑫ What kind of feet do palmipeds have?

⑬ How many completed novels did Jane Austen write?

⑭ Who was the first person to speak on the telephone?

⑮ What is the capital of Angola?

⑯ Who was voted the second 'greatest Briton of all time' in a BBC television poll?

QUIZ 84

① Who won the most Test cricket caps, Graham Gooch or Alec Stewart?

② Chantry, Harpur and Trident are all names of what?

③ What is the outer wall of a castle called?

④ What did Janet Jackson reveal during a 2004 Superbowl broadcast?

⑤ Name the first female speaker of the US House of Representatives.

⑥ What were the first door locks made from?

⑦ Who was lead vocalist with The Platters?

⑧ What is South Korea's currency?

⑨ Where was London's first airport?

⑩ What relation was Daniel Day-Lewis to playwright Arthur Miller?

⑪ Which disease was once known as 'jail fever'?

⑫ In which Italian city is *The Taming of the Shrew* set?

⑬ What are the 'Honours of Scotland'?

⑭ How many eyes does a bee have?

⑮ What does the name Berlin mean?

⑯ What was Heath Ledger's last film?

QUIZ 85

① Which castle is known as the 'Key of England'?

② What date is All Saints' Day?

③ Who played Mr Darcy in the 1940 film *Pride and Prejudice*?

④ Where is the Ashmolean Museum?

⑤ In which opera is the eponymous hero a greengrocer's assistant?

⑥ On what British rocky promontory is North Front Airport?

⑦ Which ITN reporter was killed in Iraq in 2003?

⑧ Who founded the Royal Shakespeare Company?

⑨ Which UK singer was born Pauline Matthews?

⑩ What, company wise, is 3M short for?

⑪ How is Edson Arantes do Nascimento better known?

⑫ Who said: 'Lies, damned lies and statistics'?

⑬ What nationality was the painter Piet Mondrian?

⑭ Name the other half of the 1950s comedy duo: 'Jimmy Jewell and . . .'

⑮ What was Harare formerly called?

⑯ Who buried the treasure in *Treasure Island*?

QUIZ 86

(1) Who played Flash Harry in the 2007 remake of *St Trinian's*?

(2) Who was brother to the Brontë sisters?

(3) What were previously known as the Trucial States?

(4) Who composed 'The Flight of the Bumble Bee'?

(5) In which country was John McEnroe born?

(6) Which university was founded first, Oxford or Cambridge?

(7) What commercial station was a forerunner to pirate radio?

(8) Which great British traveller and explorer died in 2003?

(9) What is Paul McCartney's first name?

(10) In archery, what colour is the centre of the target?

(11) Where are the world's tallest twin buildings?

(12) What in building terms is an RSJ?

(13) How many players are in a polo team?

(14) Who did Solomon succeed as king of Israel?

(15) What common flower is called *tournesol* in French?

(16) Which word can precede fare, tail and belt?

QUIZ 87

① What was Scotland's first university?

② Which Egyptian leader was assassinated in 1981?

③ On which river is Baghdad?

④ When is St Swithin's Day?

⑤ Radio DJ Judge Jules is the nephew of which celebrity chef?

⑥ What plants have neither flowers nor roots?

⑦ With what creative crime was Tom Keating charged in the 1970s?

⑧ What kind of dog is Dr Who's K9?

⑨ Which singer started life as Henry John Deutschendorf Jr?

⑩ Which former Kenyan leader has an airport named after him?

⑪ Which two English seats of learning have a Bridge of Sighs?

⑫ What is the collective noun for turkeys?

⑬ The fingerboard on a violin is traditionally made from what?

⑭ Who, in 1955, was the last woman to be hanged in England?

⑮ Which snake is longer, a boa constrictor or a king cobra?

⑯ Who was nicknamed 'Chairman of the Board'?

QUIZ 88

① In which country was the globe-trotting Alan Whicker born?

② Whose official residence is Walmer Castle in Kent?

③ Who produced the Beatles' hit *Let It Be*?

④ Corsica belongs to which country?

⑤ Which is furthest from Earth, Neptune or Saturn?

⑥ What was Billy the Kid's real name?

⑦ Claret is a red wine from which region?

⑧ Who was the last governor of Hong Kong?

⑨ What is a litter of piglets called?

⑩ How much on average does a human hair grow in a month?

⑪ Who commands the *Nautilus* in Jules Verne's classic tale?

⑫ Which city was home to sculptor and goldsmith Benvenuto Cellini?

⑬ Who was the first Secretary of State for Northern Ireland?

⑭ Who was motor-racing's 'Flying Finn'?

⑮ What type of lorry is named after a Hindu god?

⑯ Which English footballer was the first subject of *This Is Your Life*?

QUIZ 89
GEOGRAPHY

① Which is larger, Dartmoor or Exmoor?

② Where is Carisbrooke Castle?

③ Which country has the longest coastline in the world?

④ What was New Zealand's capital before Wellington?

⑤ What in the USA is the 'Last Frontier State'?

⑥ In which country is Transylvania?

⑦ What is the capital of Uruguay?

⑧ The George Washington Bridge spans which river?

⑨ What is the world's largest marsh?

⑩ On which river does the city of Ely stand?

⑪ What is the cooling sea breeze in Western Australia called?

⑫ Which is the largest island in the Bristol Channel?

⑬ Ellesmere Island is in which ocean?

⑭ What is the county town of Essex?

⑮ Timbuktu is in which country?

⑯ Which South American country's flag is different on each side?

QUIZ 90

① Which veteran US film director died in April 2011?

② Who wrote the 19th-century novel *The Cloister and the Hearth*?

③ What is leucocytes the medical term for?

④ Which was formed first, the Boy Scouts or the Boys Brigade?

⑤ Which bombed Spanish town inspired a Picasso painting?

⑥ What was the first artificial flavouring?

⑦ Which singer was known as the 'Little Sparrow'?

⑧ Who is St Fiacre the patron saint of?

⑨ How were Bill and Ben otherwise known?

⑩ What is the popular name for the crane fly?

⑪ Which sport has a goal 1.8m by 1.8m?

⑫ Which Australian artist painted a series of Ned Kelly pictures?

⑬ What is Sporty Spice's real name?

⑭ What species of mammal is a lemming?

⑮ Who was the 'King of Swing'?

⑯ Whose catchphrase was 'Hi there, pop pickers'?

QUIZ 91

① Which Chinese pianist has a repeatable name?

② In which war was the Battle of Brandywine Creek?

③ When was tea first brought to England: 1615, 1651, 1705?

④ In Roman numerals, what does the letter D represent?

⑤ Who was appointed chairman of the BBC Trust in 2011?

⑥ Which element has the smallest atomic weight?

⑦ What is America's longest-running sitcom?

⑧ Which poet wrote: 'Go and catch a falling star . . .'?

⑨ Which famous salad takes its name from a New York hotel?

⑩ What type of clock did Christiaan Huygens invent in 1657?

⑪ Which football club did Robert Maxwell buy?

⑫ Bronze is a combination of which two metals?

⑬ Who directed the film *Four Weddings and a Funeral*?

⑭ When was the biro pen invented: 1928, 1938 or 1948?

⑮ What Sunday paper was originally called *The New Observer*?

⑯ To which country did *Coronation Street*'s Elsie Tanner emigrate in 1984?

QUIZ 92

① When was the Israeli prime minister Yitzhak Rabin assassinated?

② How many operas comprise Wagner's *Ring* cycle?

③ What is HTH short for in Internet chat?

④ What famous sea battle began on 4 June 1942?

⑤ Who was sacked as Manchester City manager in 2009?

⑥ What was built to test the 'Big Bang' theory?

⑦ Who was knighted in 1981 for services to TV journalism?

⑧ What musical instrument offends the ear of aulophobics?

⑨ How many Oscars did *The King's Speech* win?

⑩ In *Hamlet*, who is a 'Prince of Norway'?

⑪ In which country is the city of Dumdum?

⑫ What was Kylie Minogue's first No 1 in the UK?

⑬ What is ACAS short for?

⑭ For what crime was the teenage Stephen Fry sent to jail?

⑮ What is 0.621371 of a mile?

⑯ Which English artist painted *The Derby Day*?

QUIZ 93

① What did Jimmy Wales and Larry Sanger found in 2001?

② Which is the longest river in Britain?

③ Naseby and Marston Moor were battles in which war?

④ What is the Basque separatist organization called?

⑤ In which Charles Dickens novel does Inspector Bucket appear?

⑥ In the BBC poll for the greatest 100 Britons ever, who came last?

⑦ What is the world's smallest bird?

⑧ On which river does Munich stand?

⑨ What is a beaver's home called?

⑩ How was the Hughes H4-Hercules aeroplane better known?

⑪ Which rugby player does Matt Damon portray in *Invictus*?

⑫ In which part of Los Angeles did riots break out in 1965?

⑬ Which member of The Who died in 1978?

⑭ How many stripes are there on the flag of the USA?

⑮ What is Yarg cheese coated in?

⑯ In which country was Gyles Brandreth born?

QUIZ 94

① Who was the founder of Tesco?

② In which year did the Queen Mother die?

③ Who became principal conductor of the Berlin Philharmonic in 2002?

④ How many Concorde aircraft were built?

⑤ To which country did Kaiser Wilhelm II flee in 1918?

⑥ What phrase describes a fierce contest?

⑦ 'I Could Be So Good For You' is the theme song of which TV series?

⑧ The call of which bird resembles human laughter?

⑨ Does the French tricolour have vertical or horizontal stripes?

⑩ What do the initials stand for in E M Forster?

⑪ How many pillars of wisdom did T E Lawrence have in mind?

⑫ Who was politician Shirley Williams' pacifist mother?

⑬ Who was the 'Birdman of Alcatraz'?

⑭ What is a dingle?

⑮ What are the prime numbers between 1 and 10?

⑯ Who played Young Indy in *Indiana Jones and the Last Crusade*?

QUIZ 95

① Who is the porcine ruler in George Orwell's *Animal Farm*?

② Who was appointed Leader of the House of Commons in 2010?

③ What did Barry Manilow change his surname from?

④ Which modern artist did Ed Harris portray on film in 2000?

⑤ What is Scotland's largest loch?

⑥ What is a bundle of twigs or sticks called?

⑦ Which monarch's aviary gave London's Birdcage Walk its name?

⑧ What did William Le Baron Jenney create in 1885?

⑨ What was it called and in what city was it?

⑩ Which ex-Beatle recorded 'Ding Dong, Ding Dong'?

⑪ What type of bird is a lory?

⑫ A slug's body mainly consists of what?

⑬ Complete the proverb: Rain before seven . . .

⑭ In which city was Damien Hirst born?

⑮ VOICES RANT ON is an anagram of which word?

⑯ Who designed 'The Gherkin' in London?

QUIZ 96
SPORT

1. Who were the first winners of cricket's Twenty20 Cup in 2003?

2. In rugby union, which two nations play for the Prince William Cup?

3. Which sport has a goal 3.66m wide and 2.13m high?

4. Who were the losing finalists in the 1982 FIFA World Cup?

5. When a judo referee says *hajime* what does it mean?

6. Jansher and Jahangir Khan are famous in which sport?

7. During a Formula One motor race, what does a blue flag indicate?

8. Complete the tennis duo: Newcombe and . . .

9. What is the Olympic motto (in English)?

10. Which UK prime minister had played first class cricket?

11. Whose ear did Mike Tyson notoriously bite?

12. Over what distance is the Kentucky Derby run?

13. Which athlete was nicknamed the 'Flying Scotsman'?

14. Who did David Beckham follow as a captain of England?

15. What is the name of Tasmania's Test ground?

16. In which event did Rebecca Adlington win her first gold medal at the 2008 Olympics?

QUIZ 97

① What does antediluvian literally mean?

② In which movie does Will Ferrell's character pour maple syrup over his spaghetti?

③ What is the Artful Dodger's real name?

④ What mountain range broadly separates Europe from Asia?

⑤ Which Cabinet post did Winston Churchill hold in both world wars?

⑥ What do the initials in W H Auden stand for?

⑦ In which sport do you perform a christiania?

⑧ Which singer was said to have the 'Voice of an Angel'?

⑨ What were Oxford bags?

⑩ What was John Le Carré's first published novel?

⑪ In which direction does the River Nile flow?

⑫ What returned to Earth in 2001 after 15 years?

⑬ In Shakespeare's *Hamlet*, who is Ophelia's father?

⑭ Who made his name as television's *Troubleshooter*?

⑮ The sagebrush is the floral emblem of which US state?

⑯ Which Hollywood star was born John Uhler III?

QUIZ 98

① What occurs once in a minute, twice in a week and once in a year?

② New Caledonia is an overseas territory of which European country?

③ In which year did Prince Andrew and Sarah Ferguson marry?

④ Who did Homer Simpson think Tony Blair was?

⑤ What does the name Dublin mean?

⑥ In what profession did Delia Smith begin her working life?

⑦ What does CNN stand for?

⑧ Where in Australia is Canberra located?

⑨ Hannibal was the military leader of which ancient city?

⑩ What did President Johnson award Forrest Gump in the film?

⑪ For which league football club did comedian Des O'Connor play?

⑫ Which two Beatles were left-handed?

⑬ Who is the author of the Inspector Alleyn books?

⑭ Which English king inherited the throne when nine months old?

⑮ What is the world's fastest flying insect?

⑯ What is a narrow inlet of the sea is called?

QUIZ 99

① What is a Jewish skullcap called?

② What is the mule a cross between?

③ What is the killing of one's brother or sister called?

④ Dubris was the Roman name for which English town?

⑤ How is the operatic character Cio-Cio San better known?

⑥ What does a hygrometer measure?

⑦ Lemurs, bushbabies and marmosets are all what?

⑧ What physical disability was Lord Byron born with?

⑨ Which popular song comes from Chopin's *Fantaisie Impromptu*?

⑩ What did the Beckhams name their first daughter?

⑪ Which sporting activity involves pikes, tucks and twists?

⑫ Which London Underground line was opened in 1968

⑬ Who was Maureen Lipman's playwright husband?

⑭ What was The Wurzels only No 1 hit?

⑮ What does the Roman numeral L stand for?

⑯ What word describes a shallow lake of salt water?

QUIZ 100

① What is the more familiar term for calcimine?

② Who was Mickey Rooney's first wife?

③ Bacon, Pinkerton and Gwen are varieties of what fruit?

④ What is the Turkish anise-flavoured drink called?

⑤ Who played Alfred the butler in the film *Batman Begins*?

⑥ What nationality was the jeweller Fabergé?

⑦ What is a tumulus?

⑧ Where was *Queen Mary 2* built?

⑨ Which is further north, Manchester or Sheffield?

⑩ 'Go Now' was a major hit for which 1960s pop group?

⑪ How many 'Road' movies did Bob Hope and Bing Crosby make?

⑫ Who wrote the play *Juno and the Paycock*?

⑬ What is molten rock below the earth's crust called?

⑭ In the biblical story, whom did the Queen of Sheba visit?

⑮ Who invented the railway sleeping car?

⑯ Laphroaig whisky comes from which Scottish island?

QUIZ 101

① What is the first name of the French artist Cézanne?

② What is the old name for sulphur?

③ Who in 1991 became France's first woman prime minister?

④ Becquerels are a unit of what?

⑤ Patagonia is a region of which country?

⑥ What is the fictional Dr Watson's first name?

⑦ Which ex-Test cricketer was jailed in 2009 for drug smuggling?

⑧ What became illegal on the London Underground in 1984?

⑨ Love apple is an old-fashioned name for what?

⑩ What is the art of shaping hedges called?

⑪ Whose statue was unveiled in London's Parliament Square in 2007?

⑫ Eric Burden was lead singer of which 60s group?

⑬ What is the horn of a rhinoceros made from?

⑭ What does *Götterdämmerung* mean?

⑮ Who wrote the play *Man and Superman*?

⑯ What is a culverin?

QUIZ 102

① Who were rugby's final Tri-Nations champions?

② What is biltong?

③ Who did Penelope Cruz marry in 2010?

④ A glow-worm is not a worm – what is it?

⑤ Which sea is at the northern end of the Suez Canal?

⑥ Which singer changed his name to Yusef Islam?

⑦ What is the major prize at the Venice Film Festival?

⑧ *Eboracum* is the Roman name for which English city?

⑨ Who was the last of the Plantagenet kings?

⑩ The Kariba Dam is on which African river?

⑪ Who was the first 'royal' to be interviewed on TV?

⑫ What is the technical name for bell ringing?

⑬ Where does a 'demersal' creature live?

⑭ What does the W stand for in George W Bush?

⑮ Which two letters are worth ten points each in Scrabble?

⑯ What does the word vernal relate to?

QUIZ 103

① Who was Michael Jackson's personal doctor?

② In which city were the 2010 Commonwealth Games staged?

③ Who was the first host of TV's *Bargain Hunt*?

④ Which 19th-century novel begins: 'Call me Ishmael.'?

⑤ Who founded the Slimbridge bird sanctuary?

⑥ How tall are the numbers on Big Ben?

⑦ On which racecourse is the Scottish Grand National run?

⑧ Which rock star once worked as a gravedigger?

⑨ In which country is the source of the White Nile?

⑩ Which Netherlands city is famous for its porcelain?

⑪ Which French philosopher wrote: 'I think therefore I am'?

⑫ What does the Japanese word *kamikaze* mean?

⑬ What is the calendar used by most Western nations?

⑭ Which butterfly shares the name of a punctuation mark?

⑮ What was comedian Benny Hill's job before show business?

⑯ Who composed the music for the ballet *Billy the Kid*?

QUIZ 104
CINEMA & TV

① Michael Caine's brother Stanley appeared with him in which film?

② Which *Harry Potter* star enrolled at Oxford University in 2011?

③ Whose TV comic character is Mr Cholmondley-Warner?

④ What sort of fish is Nemo in *Finding Nemo*?

⑤ What is the name of the prison in *Porridge*?

⑥ In which film did Meryl Streep make her big screen debut?

⑦ *Till Death Us Do Part* became what in the USA?

⑧ What is the name of the central character in *Brighton Rock*?

⑨ Which US actor's real name is Alphonso Joseph d'Abruzzo?

⑩ Who plays Miss Babs in 'Acorn Antiques'?

⑪ In which western does John Cleese play a sheriff?

⑫ Who plays Captain Hastings in *Poirot*?

⑬ Complete the film title: '*Five Graves to . . .*'

⑭ Which TV cop is based in Ystad?

⑮ In which film does Gene Kelly dance on roller skates?

⑯ What film role did Donald Pleasence, Telly Savalas and Charles Gray share?

QUIZ 105

① Whose autobiography was *Lies and Boogie-Woogie Boasts*?

② In cockney rhyming slang, what are 'Harvey Nichols'?

③ Who was the first author to win the Booker Prize twice?

④ When did Ceylon become Sri Lanka?

⑤ Which 1954 battle ended France's occupation of Vietnam?

⑥ What is the name of the Obama family dog acquired in 2009?

⑦ Who wrote the song 'I Say A Little Prayer For You'?

⑧ What are the colours of the Italian flag, left to right?

⑨ What do the Four Horsemen of the Apocalypse represent?

⑩ What is the collective name for magpies?

⑪ In which year did UK National Service end?

⑫ Which Nazi leader flew to Britain in 1941?

⑬ Which aviator was called the 'Lone Eagle'?

⑭ How many chambers does the heart have?

⑮ What is the largest island in Asia?

⑯ Which UK weather forecaster's name is in the title of a song?

QUIZ 106

1. What was Sister Sledge's 1979 hit?

2. What type of institute is Chatham House?

3. What is a fashion item and a former nuclear testing site?

4. Which gland produces insulin?

5. Who invented the lightning conductor?

6. What do the initials stand for in J G Ballard?

7. From what kind of wood was the Kon-Tiki raft made?

8. What is the largest island in the Mediterranean?

9. Which war came to an end in August 1988?

10. Whose last word was 'Rosebud'?

11. Which German spa gave its name to an item of men's headwear?

12. What is the knife carried by Gurkha soldiers called?

13. Which artist painted his *Bedroom in Arles*?

14. Metrology is the study of what?

15. Which English lord fled the scene of the crime in 1974?

16. Who sang 'Goodness Gracious Me' in the film *The Millionairess*?

QUIZ 107

① Who was the last Norman king of England?

② In cockney rhyming slang, what is 'Richard the Third'?

③ Which is the only Charles Dickens novel with a female narrator?

④ Who has more ribs, a man or a woman?

⑤ What is carrageen also known as?

⑥ Which UK statesman cut his throat with a letter opener in 1822?

⑦ What, under the sea, do the initials FLAG stand for?

⑧ Who was the child with a magic talking piano?

⑨ What did Stevie Wonder lose after a car crash in 1973?

⑩ Who wrote *Portrait of the Artist as a Young Dog*?

⑪ What song do they strip to in *The Full Monty*?

⑫ How high is the crossbar of a rugby goalpost?

⑬ Which Lizzie allegedly chopped up her parents with an axe?

⑭ The Reichenbach Falls are in which country?

⑮ Who was 2009 BBC Sports Personality of the Year?

⑯ Where was Captain James Cook killed in 1779?

QUIZ 108

① Who was longer on the throne, George IV or William IV?

② In the song, what was sent on the eleventh day of Christmas?

③ What are invertebrates?

④ Who was the 'Acid Bath Murderer'?

⑤ Which UK sporting charity was founded in 1950?

⑥ In which country is Machu Picchu?

⑦ Which treaty was signed at the end of World War One?

⑧ What does a notaphile collect?

⑨ Where did the game of Fives originate?

⑩ What type of fruit is a 'Beauty of Bath'?

⑪ Who created the Cornish detective Wycliffe?

⑫ What criminal career did the 18th-century Anne Bonny pursue?

⑬ Which Mama Cass song was used in the Meg Ryan film *French Kiss*?

⑭ How many players in an Australian Rules team?

⑮ What was the RAF previously called?

⑯ Who was Malcolm Little by the time he died in 1965?

QUIZ 109

① What sport is Hugh Grant addicted to?

② What means a layer of fat and a person sobbing?

③ Who rescued Richard Branson's mother from a fire in 2011?

④ What do the initials stand for in T E Lawrence?

⑤ Who stopped being an Animal in 1965?

⑥ During the Boer War who was known as 'Uncle Paul'?

⑦ Whose military defences were called the Maginot Line?

⑧ How many times were Torvill and Dean World Ice Dance Champions?

⑨ The Giant's Causeway is in which Irish county?

⑩ Which golf 'Open' was introduced first, the British or US?

⑪ In which English city was Guy Fawkes born?

⑫ Al Gore was the US senator for which state?

⑬ In which country are the Shakta Pantjukhina caves?

⑭ Which character in *Cats* sings 'Memory' ?

⑮ What is the cube root of 64?

⑯ What are small balls of lead fired from a cannon?

QUIZ 110

① Where did ice hockey originate?

② Whose escape from Devil's Island was a film with Steve McQueen?

③ Which French monarch was known as the 'Sun King'?

④ Where is the Menin Gate?

⑤ In which film does Bing Crosby sing 'True Love'?

⑥ What can be a short jacket or a dance?

⑦ Who wrote *Whisky Galore*?

⑧ What does a necrologist write?

⑨ What does the abbreviation NAAFI stand for?

⑩ Who composed the theme music for the film *Kill Bill*?

⑪ Which spinner was Shane Warne's 1000th international wicket?

⑫ What do silkworms feed on?

⑬ Add the showbiz surname: Alec, Stephen and William . . .?

⑭ Who said: 'Power is the ultimate aphrodisiac'?

⑮ 'Parmentier' means garnished or cooked with which vegetable?

⑯ What is the name of Florence's famous bridge?

QUIZ 111
SCIENCE & NATURE

① What nationality was psychoanalyst Carl Jung?

② Scurvy is caused by a lack of what?

③ In computer speak, what is a PDF?

④ What is the common name for calcium oxide?

⑤ The brambling is a member of which family of British birds?

⑥ What is your trachea?

⑦ Who devised a code of medical ethics circa 400 BC?

⑧ How many satellites has Jupiter?

⑨ What is the collective name for rhinoceros?

⑩ If you are thalassophobic what are you afraid of?

⑪ How many teeth does a sea urchin have?

⑫ What is another name for a thrip?

⑬ Diamonds are a crystalline form of what?

⑭ Would a lake on Mars be freezing or boiling?

⑮ What does the Scoville Scale measure?

⑯ Which mathematical system uses only the digits 0 and 1?

QUIZ 112

① What can be a viral infection or a low temperature?

② Which teenage singer faced a paternity suit from a fan in 2011?

③ Which country elected the world's first female prime minister?

④ Who composed the opera *Peter Grimes*?

⑤ Ludo is the children's version of which game?

⑥ Which great American writer died in 2009?

⑦ Who was the first Formula One world champion?

⑧ Where in Egypt is the Great Pyramid?

⑨ What is the county town of Dorset?

⑩ What number on the Beaufort scale denotes a gale?

⑪ Who wrote: 'Brevity is the soul of wit'?

⑫ Which UK singing star of the 1950s was born Richard Bryce?

⑬ Which US president's widow became a UN delegate?

⑭ Russell Brand supports which football team?

⑮ The Black Prince was the son of which English king?

⑯ In which US national park is the geyser 'Old Faithful'?

QUIZ 113

① Who invented the cotton gin?

② What is the Italian Grand Prix motor racing circuit?

③ Who is the central character in George Orwell's *1984*?

④ What does the abbreviation SHAPE stand for?

⑤ With whom did Katherine Hepburn have a long love affair?

⑥ What is the last letter of the modern Greek alphabet?

⑦ What were Frank Sinatra's given names?

⑧ Who printed the first book in English?

⑨ Who were Buster's Diaries told to?

⑩ What is Prince's real first name?

⑪ Who pioneered the use of frozen foods?

⑫ What is the smallest of the Channel Islands open to the public?

⑬ Which cricketer was nicknamed 'Zulu'?

⑭ What is the Israeli parliament called?

⑮ Where is the longest champagne bar in Europe?

⑯ Which MP was killed by an IRA bomb in the House of Commons car park in 1979?

QUIZ 114

① What relation was Queen Victoria to George IV?

② What are long matted coils of hair called?

③ Whose autobiography was *The Good, the Bad and the Bubbly*?

④ Which bluegrass singer teamed up with Robert Plant in 2007?

⑤ In which sport might you do a triffus?

⑥ Which Disney film features the song 'Topsy Turvy'?

⑦ In which city does the annual Oktoberfest take place?

⑧ What is the French stock exchange called?

⑨ How many of Queen Anne's five children survived her?

⑩ In Greek mythology, who had the golden touch?

⑪ Which of the play-writing Shaffer twins wrote *Sleuth*?

⑫ In which year was the Sony Walkman launched?

⑬ Who designed the 1960s Kipper tie?

⑭ With what is Baron Kelvin the physicist associated?

⑮ Which sport does the 'Essex Exocet' play?

⑯ In which US state is the Painted Desert?

QUIZ 115

① What long-running TV role did Jay Silverheels play?

② Where was Billy Butlin's first holiday camp?

③ Charles Eames was most famous for designing a what?

④ Who played Ronnie Branning in *EastEnders*?

⑤ *Papillon* is French for what?

⑥ Who was the Peloponnesian War between?

⑦ What are Tiger Wood's forenames?

⑧ Who wrote *Confessions of an English Opium-Eater*?

⑨ Complete the song title: 'Maxwell's ... Hammer'.

⑩ Who captained the 1974 British Lions in South Africa?

⑪ What date is midway between winter and spring?

⑫ Which writer proposed as her epitaph: 'Excuse my dust'?

⑬ What is an Archimedes screw used for?

⑭ Which Egyptian king abdicated in 1952?

⑮ What was the name of the dog on the HMV label?

⑯ Which Catherine Tate character routinely asks, 'Am I bovverd?'?

QUIZ 116

① What can be a fish or a light quick stroke?

② Which literary fiction prize was launched in 1996?

③ Which Frankish king was crowned Holy Roman Emperor in 800?

④ What can be Bearded, Blue or Coal?

⑤ Which daily radio programme is condensed to WATO?

⑥ Who wrote *The Legend of Sleepy Hollow*?

⑦ In which country is the World Ice Golf Championship held?

⑧ Which fast bowler was nicknamed 'Whispering Death'?

⑨ What side of a ship is starboard, left or right?

⑩ Which sexy couple had their 1969 hit banned by the BBC?

⑪ In which sport does the tee sit in the centre of the house?

⑫ Which English operatic festival was founded in 1934?

⑬ Who was Wayne Rooney's best man?

⑭ What type of engines have afterburners?

⑮ Who did the Germans call *Der Bingle*?

⑯ Manama is the capital of which Middle Eastern country?

QUIZ 117

① Whose motto is *Per ardua ad astra*?

② And what does it mean?

③ What is the full name of Ronnie Barker's character in *Porridge*?

④ Who was Johnny Cash's other half?

⑤ What is a group of rocks or boulders on top of a hill called?

⑥ Add the sporting surname: John and Justin . . .

⑦ What is a Scottish clan chief called?

⑧ To which company of actors did William Shakespeare belong?

⑨ Which 18th-century landscape gardener was sure to get the job done?

⑩ Who did Renate Blauel marry on Valentine's Day, 1984?

⑪ What do ichthyologists study?

⑫ What did John McAdam invent in 1815?

⑬ What are Gold Murderer and Thunder & Lightning?

⑭ In its original French, what does the word 'biscuit' mean?

⑮ What do the wartime initials ATS stand for?

⑯ Who played the title role in *The Life and Death of Peter Sellers*?

QUIZ 118

① Who was the last British king to sack a prime minister?

② What is the national assembly of the Church of England?

③ Who is not always affectionately known as the 'Beast of Bolsover'?

④ What are 'bed and breakfasts' called in France?

⑤ Who was the first British black trade-union leader?

⑥ Which poet's ashes were buried at East Coker in Somerset?

⑦ Who headed the military coup in Argentina in 1981?

⑧ In chess, which piece can move only in straight lines?

⑨ 'A Whole New World' was the hope of which tabloid couple in 2006?

⑩ What does the 'Bishop's Ring' encircle?

⑪ What was the wartime RAF squadron 617 nicknamed?

⑫ At which racecourse was the Derby staged during World War Two?

⑬ Whose book *Fathers & Sons* was published in 2008?

⑭ Which jockey was stripped of his OBE in 1988?

⑮ Who was US president at the start of the 21st century?

⑯ Where in the UK is Scatsa airport?

QUIZ 119
MUSIC

① Chris Lowe and Neil Tennant are better known as what?

② With whose British jazz band did Ottilie Patterson sing?

③ Which group were 'Alone On Christmas Day' in 2004?

④ Who was the founder of Island Records?

⑤ 'Here Comes The Judge' was whose only UK hit?

⑥ Whose music for *Atonement* won an Oscar in 2008?

⑦ Who is Radiohead's lead vocalist?

⑧ Take That and Lulu had a 1993 hit with what song?

⑨ Bernard Webb was the pseudonym of which Beatle?

⑩ What 2010 song raised money for Haiti's earthquake victims?

⑪ Cheryl Cole featured in a 1980s TV commercial for what?

⑫ What is Janet Jackson's middle name?

⑬ Who was the founder of the New Christy Minstrels?

⑭ Which US musician was equally famous as conductor and composer?

⑮ How is Yvette Stevens more exotically known?

⑯ In the 1968 song, whose satchel did The Hollies carry?

QUIZ 120

① Fishoek is a wine-growing region in which country?

② What was the chief magistrate in Venice called?

③ In cockney rhyming slang, what is 'Doctor Crippen'?

④ Cocksfoot, Timothy and Tufted Hair are all types of what?

⑤ What was Elton John fitted with in 1999?

⑥ Which champion snooker player was nicknamed 'the Silver Fox'?

⑦ What is a USB flash drive?

⑧ Which fish had a starring role in a 1988 hit movie?

⑨ What was Michael Jackson's first solo record?

⑩ Which Great War poet wrote 'Anthem for Doomed Youth'?

⑪ In which Olympics did Mary Peters win a gold medal?

⑫ What does BUPA stand for?

⑬ Who painted *Dedham Lock and Mill*?

⑭ Which British king was known as 'Farmer George'?

⑮ What is the civilian equivalent of the Victoria Cross?

⑯ From whom did Roman Abramovich buy Chelsea FC?

QUIZ 121

1. Where do Bajans live?

2. What is a Water Soldier?

3. In which county are the ruins of Fountains Abbey?

4. What was the name of Don Quixote's horse?

5. The Vistula flows through which capital city?

6. On which day of the year did Dean Martin die?

7. What is the English translation of *Veni, vidi, vici*?

8. In which US state is Lake Okeechobee?

9. Who said: 'Religion is the opium of the people'?

10. The film *Shine* was about which Australian classical pianist?

11. For which hillside feature is Cerne Abbas famous?

12. Who directed the film *Key Largo*?

13. What is at the centre of the flag of Israel?

14. The Yellowstone National Park is in which three states?

15. What did the Savoy Big Five become?

16. Which British coin carries the inscription 'Standing on the shoulders of giants'?

QUIZ 122

① On which river is Perth, Australia?

② In *As Time Goes By*, what is Jean's agency called?

③ Who was the first female head of MI5?

④ How many players in a Gaelic football team?

⑤ What does an odometer measure?

⑥ Whose 1942 report paved the way for the NHS?

⑦ Who wrote *The Andromeda Strain*?

⑧ What is US actor Michael Keaton's real name?

⑨ In former times, Tyburn was a place of what?

⑩ What is the name of Billy Bunter's school?

⑪ In Greek mythology, who was god of the sky?

⑫ What short-lived 1980s soap opera was set in Manchester?

⑬ How many hostages were killed at the 1972 Munich Olympics?

⑭ In which year did the USA enter World War Two?

⑮ What was the name of the first Rolls Royce?

⑯ Which European country's currency is the Lev?

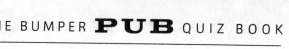

QUIZ 123

1. What do the broadcasting initials RCA stand for?

2. What can be a furnace or to move steadily ahead?

3. Which theatre was unearthed in London in 1988?

4. What is the largest town on the island of Jersey?

5. Which petrol brand claimed to put a 'tiger in the tank'?

6. What unit of currency is used in Liechtenstein?

7. What 1950 UK film gave rise to a long-running TV police series?

8. What was the name of the senior Yellowcoat in *Hi-de-Hi*?

9. Who was the first editor of *Private Eye*?

10. What did Queen Victoria's husband die of?

11. Which broadcaster's autobiography was titled *Where's Harry*?

12. Fluellen is a character in which Shakespeare play?

13. Who became Speaker of the House of Commons in 2009?

14. Which comet was highly visible from Earth in 1997?

15. In Morse Code, what letter is a single dot?

16. What iconic 1960s boutique did Barbara Hulanicki found?

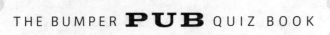

QUIZ 124

1. What shaped mark does an adder have on its head?

2. Who was Lyndon Johnson's vice-president?

3. What sport is the theme of the 1984 film *The Natural*?

4. Where was St Paul born?

5. Name the only US president to serve two non-consecutive terms.

6. Mozart's K626 is better known as what?

7. Who were known as the 'Old Contemptibles'?

8. What is the world's longest mountain range?

9. Which TV and radio quiz panelist committed suicide in 1980?

10. 2011 was the Chinese year of the what?

11. Who was the male star of *The Seven Year Itch*?

12. What staple food item was first canned in 1880?

13. Which county cricket side is based at Sophia Gardens?

14. What is the fifth letter of the Greek alphabet?

15. Which famous English poet was only 4ft 6in tall?

16. In *Downton Abbey*, what relation is Matthew Crawley to the Earl of Grantham?

QUIZ 125

① Whose autobiography was entitled *Where's the Rest of Me*?

② What does the Italian word *ciabatta* mean?

③ Jack the Ripper is cockney rhyming slang for what?

④ What did the Gilbert Islands become?

⑤ When was Nelson Mandela released from prison?

⑥ How many players in a baseball team?

⑦ What word describes a person of wide-ranging knowledge?

⑧ Who did Harold Macmillan succeed as prime minister?

⑨ In what sport is the egg-beater kick performed?

⑩ To where did London Bridge move in 1968?

⑪ Which gas forms nearly 80% of the earth's atmosphere?

⑫ The actress Lillie Langtry was which king's mistress?

⑬ Sir Andrew Aguecheek is a character in which Shakespeare play?

⑭ What bird is also known as a sea parrot?

⑮ Which footballer was BBC Sports Personality of the Year in 1990?

⑯ What colours are the German flag, in descending order?

QUIZ 126
HISTORY

① In which year did the Vietnam War end?

....

② Who commanded the British fleet at the Battle of Jutland?

....

③ What massacre took place in South Africa in 1960?

....

④ Who became German president in 1932?

....

⑤ Which king of England was crowned on Christmas Day?

....

⑥ How old was William Pitt when he became prime minister in 1783?

....

⑦ What did Elizabeth Fry reform?

....

⑧ How was Josip Broz better known?

....

⑨ Who in 1906 became the first US president to travel abroad?

....

⑩ Which Middle East war broke out in October 1973?

....

⑪ Who was the last king of Italy?

....

⑫ Which two great military adversaries were born in 1769?

....

⑬ Which club was a driving force in the French Revolution?

....

⑭ Who was known as the 'Hanging Judge'?

....

⑮ Where in Australia was outlaw Ned Kelly hanged in 1880?

....

⑯ Who was the first Roman emperor?

....

QUIZ 127

① Catherine Morland is the heroine of which Jane Austen novel?

② What did the UK and Iceland fight over in the 1960s?

③ Which London football club is older, Chelsea or Spurs?

④ What part of the body is the hallux?

⑤ Which is the longest cathedral in Europe?

⑥ In which year did the Great Smog engulf London?

⑦ Which TV fashion guru once weighed 21 stone?

⑧ What is an angle more than 90° called?

⑨ Which poet was murdered by Spanish Nationalists in 1936?

⑩ What day follows Shrove Tuesday?

⑪ Where was a barrelman stationed on board a ship?

⑫ With which art form is André Kertesz associated?

⑬ Light, Home and Third were all what?

⑭ What is the plural of mongoose?

⑮ Who is Queen Mab?

⑯ What is further north, Ayr or Dumfries?

QUIZ 128

① What was the UK's first full-colour tabloid newspaper?

② How is the wild hyacinth more popularly known?

③ What type of musical instrument is the Chinese sheng?

④ In which year did the original Covent Garden close?

⑤ Who played the boy in the 1953 film *Shane*?

⑥ In proofreading, what does 'stet' mean?

⑦ Does the origin of the word aristocracy mean 'best' or 'rich'?

⑧ What does the K stand for in Jerome K Jerome?

⑨ Who was the first American World Chess Champion?

⑩ What came first, the Bronze Age or the Iron Age?

⑪ Which actress was born Ilyena Vasilievna Mironov?

⑫ What nationality was the Surrealist painter René Magritte?

⑬ What is the collective noun for guardians?

⑭ Astronomically speaking, what is a bolide?

⑮ What is one's 'Alma Mater'?

⑯ Who was born Edna May Beazley in the city of Wagga Wagga?

QUIZ 129

① Which footballer's nickname was 'Captain Marvel'?

② Who played 'Boss' Tweed in *Gangs of New York*?

③ The Mercalli scale is used for measuring what?

④ How is the Shaftesbury Memorial Fountain in London better known?

⑤ The phrase 'brave new world' comes from which Shakespeare play?

⑥ Name the car ferry that sank off Zeebrugge in 1987.

⑦ When was the 'Winter of Discontent'?

⑧ Abbotsford was which famous Scottish writer's home?

⑨ In which city is Jim Morrison of The Doors buried?

⑩ What on your face is the philtrum?

⑪ How many cities are there in Greater London?

⑫ In what country do they dance the 'horah'?

⑬ How many British monarchs separate William III and William IV?

⑭ Which item of headgear is made from the sola plant?

⑮ What scissors give a zigzag edge when cutting?

⑯ Which singer opened a music academy for underprivileged children in 2005?

QUIZ 130

① What does 'Third Reich' mean?

② How many Boer Wars were there?

③ What variety of fruit is a Suffolk Thorn?

④ Which planet has a moon called Larissa?

⑤ What are the three primary colours of light?

⑥ Whose anti-war work, *State Britain*, won the 2007 Turner Prize?

⑦ Who wrote and sang the theme for the film *Absolute Beginners*?

⑧ Who did Shane Warne romantically bowl over in 2011?

⑨ What does the name Barbara mean?

⑩ In Greek mythology, who was the god of the North Wind?

⑪ What relation was Christopher Lee to Ian Fleming?

⑫ Who said that a man tired of London was tired of life?

⑬ What was the currency of Finland before the euro?

⑭ Where did Cassius Clay win his Olympic gold medal?

⑮ What was the eldest son of the king of France called?

⑯ Who is the author of the *Raj Quartet*?

QUIZ 131

① Who did Allen Konigsberg become?

② Who wrote the novel *No Country for Old Men*?

③ What was the name of Odysseus' dog?

④ Destroying Angel and Wood Woolly Foot are types of what?

⑤ What was Team Britain's gold medal tally at Beijing?

⑥ The sackbut was an early form of what?

⑦ What was Westlife's first No 1 hit?

⑧ What is the Duke of Bedford's family seat?

⑨ Who slaughtered whom at the massacre of Glencoe in 1692?

⑩ What is performed every ten years at Oberammergau?

⑪ Which Hindu god of wisdom has an elephant's head?

⑫ Who was the first black African to win an Olympic gold medal?

⑬ Who assassinated Martin Luther King Jr?

⑭ Which birds never need to drink fresh water?

⑮ Dale Winton played a game show presenter in which film?

⑯ Which organization won the Nobel Peace Prize in 1999?

QUIZ 132

① What was Benito Mussolini's profession before politics?

② Who was the founder of the ill-fated *Today* newspaper?

③ What is the largest Ferris wheel in Europe?

④ Which musical instrument did Larry Adler play?

⑤ In the Chinese calendar which animal follows the sheep?

⑥ What was Charlie Chaplin's first fully talking film?

⑦ Whose catchphrase is 'What's up, Doc'?

⑧ Cinnabar is the common ore of which metal?

⑨ What relation is Queen Elizabeth II to Queen Alexandra?

⑩ How old was Dusty Springfield when she died?

⑪ The volcano Paricutin is in which country?

⑫ King William II was killed whilst hunting in which forest?

⑬ Which French artist painted *The Card Players*?

⑭ When was the first Henley Royal Regatta: 1839, 1849 or 1859?

⑮ Who is Andrew Lloyd Webber's cello-playing brother?

⑯ What is the formula to find the area of a circle?

QUIZ 133

① Whose Hollywood mansion was called Pickfair?

② Which national newspaper was launched in 1964?

③ In the novel, what is Lolita's actual name?

④ What does the Russian word *perestroika* mean?

⑤ Which conductor founded the London Philharmonic in 1932?

⑥ On what island does Bond villain Dr No reside?

⑦ Which famous All Black was sent off at Murrayfield in 1967?

⑧ What in agricultural terms does GM stand for?

⑨ Don Quixote was a man from which part of Spain?

⑩ How many European football clubs did Bobby Robson manage?

⑪ Who is South Africa's foremost playwright?

⑫ Which singing star died during a UK tour in 2006?

⑬ Samuel de Champlain founded which French colony?

⑭ What do the initials stand for in J M Barrie?

⑮ What are young salmon or trout called?

⑯ Which great British actor died in 2008 at the age of 86?

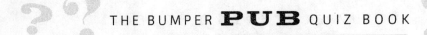

QUIZ 134
GEOGRAPHY

① Where is St Magnus, the UK's most northerly cathedral?

② On which river is Perth in Scotland?

③ Name the marshland on England's southeast coast.

④ What is France's longest river?

⑤ Which Israeli city is on the slopes of Mt Carmel?

⑥ What does UAE stand for?

⑦ Which river flows north and south of the Equator?

⑧ The Fox Islands are part of which larger archipelago?

⑨ Which two colours are on the flag of Ukraine?

⑩ What is a cataract?

⑪ Which US state is known as the Diamond State?

⑫ In which country is the port of Beira?

⑬ Gimpo International Airport is in which country?

⑭ What town is at the Pacific end of the Panama Canal?

⑮ Which is larger, Norway or Sweden?

⑯ What is the driest inhabited continent on earth?

QUIZ 135

① What was the rocket developed by Britain in the 1950s?

② How long did the Hundred Years War last?

③ Which Benjamin Britten opera is from a story by Herman Melville?

④ What instrument did Linda McCartney play in the band Wings?

⑤ Which postwar prime minister's dog was called Paddy?

⑥ Who compiled *The Devil's Dictionary*?

⑦ Which card game is based on the stock market?

⑧ What is a *kugelhopf*: a cake, kid's toy or hunting horn?

⑨ Of which country was Brian Boru king?

⑩ How many legs does a Harvestman have?

⑪ Who asked that his portrait depict 'warts and everything'?

⑫ 'In the Depths of the Temple' is a famous duet from which opera?

⑬ Who did starlet Valerie Solanis attempt to kill in 1968?

⑭ Who was the last prime minister of Northern Ireland?

⑮ When was London Zoo founded: 1828, 1838 or 1848?

⑯ Which game takes its name from the Chinese for 'sparrow'?

QUIZ 136

① Which 19th-century French writer died of caffeine poisoning?

② Brick, Flint and Salt are all names of what?

③ What was *Spitting Image*'s nonsensical 1986 hit?

④ Which England batsman scored a century on debut in 2009?

⑤ Who succeeded John Major as leader of the Conservatives?

⑥ Which play begins: 'Now is the winter of our discontent . . .'?

⑦ What do Americans call men's braces?

⑧ Which great British Empire builder committed suicide in 1774?

⑨ An hendecagon has how many sides?

⑩ Who was the first British driver to win a Grand Prix?

⑪ What are Saturn's rings made of?

⑫ Who said: 'Superman don't need no seatbelt'?

⑬ Add the showbiz surname: Julia and Nadia . . .

⑭ Who wrote and made famous the song 'La Mer'?

⑮ Who did Vladimir Putin pick to succeed him in 2009?

⑯ Which English 19th-century classic is subtitled: 'A Novel Without a Hero'?

QUIZ 137

① How much of Richard I's ten-year reign was spent in England?

② Which is the only English county with two separate coasts?

③ Who sold Alaska to the USA?

④ What does *ante bellum* mean?

⑤ In which card game does actor Omar Sharif excel?

⑥ Favourite and Figaro are varieties of which vegetable?

⑦ FIENDISH is an anagram of what word?

⑧ What academic degree is a DCL?

⑨ Bucks Fizz won the 1981 Eurovision Song Contest with what song?

⑩ Which war concluded with the 1713 Treaty of Utrecht?

⑪ Add the showbiz surname: Patrick and Don . . .

⑫ What traditionally denotes a 20th wedding anniversary?

⑬ The Shenandoah is a tributary of which American river?

⑭ Who wrote *The Gulag Archipelago*?

⑮ What is the Bishop of Durham's official residence?

⑯ Which US legend did Richard Widmark play in *The Alamo*?

QUIZ 138

① What is Mickey Mouse called in Italy?

② In which game do you find Double Ducks or Quacks?

③ What does a pteridologist study?

④ Who did Oscar Wilde call 'The Divine Sarah'?

⑤ Which was London's first suspension bridge?

⑥ Who became manager of Coventry City FC in 1961?

⑦ How did the first man in space, Yuri Gagarin, die?

⑧ What do the initials stand for in W B Yeats?

⑨ Who is regarded as the father of modern economics?

⑩ What is a Boston crab?

⑪ What are the three kinds of teeth (excluding false!)?

⑫ Hodge was a traditional name for what type of worker?

⑬ Where did the Crystal Palace originally stand?

⑭ What date is St Andrews Day?

⑮ Who was Billy Joel singing about in 'Uptown Girl'?

⑯ What is the largest tree fruit in the world?

QUIZ 139

① What is the most senior back bench MP in Parliament called?

② Which London Underground station has the longest escalator?

③ What is the French variant of backgammon?

④ Which English queen was called the 'Flanders Mare'?

⑤ What describes an unwanted authorial hiatus?

⑥ Which English conductor had a 75th birthday concert in 2009?

⑦ What colour are the flowers of wild garlic?

⑧ Which US soap was a spin-off from *Dallas*?

⑨ What are *pomodori*?

⑩ What nationality was the composer Alban Berg?

⑪ Who was the American TV lifestyle guru sent to jail in 2004?

⑫ What is rolled in the Canadian sport of birling?

⑬ What does the word jocose mean?

⑭ What is a three-dimensional, laser-generated image called?

⑮ Who was the 'Voice of Rugby' who died in 2010?

⑯ What is 999 in Roman numerals?

QUIZ 140

① Who turned a can of soup into a work of art?

② Which bird is also known as a Mavis?

③ Who played Reggie Perrin second time around?

④ *Like A Virgin* was the unlikely named hit album for whom?

⑤ Who was the first British composer to receive a peerage?

⑥ To which other animal species is the okapi related?

⑦ Who was the first woman created by the Greek gods?

⑧ What are the spots on a domino called?

⑨ Which outspoken UK journalist and broadcaster died in 2004?

⑩ Who attacked British ships in the River Medway in 1667?

⑪ What is the name of Hugh Grant's character in *Notting Hill*?

⑫ Whose defiant act in 1955 started a bus boycott in Alabama?

⑬ On which lake was Donald Campbell killed in 1967?

⑭ In the Bible, who is the wife of King Ahab?

⑮ Which Spanish artist set up his own museum in Figueres?

⑯ What was the forerunner of the musket?

QUIZ 141
SPORT

1. What brand were the balls for the 2011 Rugby World Cup?

2. Where was the first FA Cup final played?

3. And who were the winners?

4. In golf, what is an 'eagle'?

5. Who was the first World Chess Champion?

6. What in American football is known as a 'bomb'?

7. Which South African bowler was like a 'frog in a blender'?

8. Who was the first women's World Darts Champion?

9. Which sport was founded in Britain in 1895?

10. How many Grand Slam singles titles did Pete Sampras win?

11. What racing track is rebuilt every year?

12. How old was Ian Botham when Geoff Boycott made his Test debut?

13. Where did snooker originate?

14. Who did Arsène Wenger succeed as Arsenal manager?

15. Which golfer was nicknamed 'The Big Easy'?

16. How many Olympic gold medals did Tarzan win?

QUIZ 142

1. 'It's Raining Men' featured on the soundtrack of which 2001 film?

2. Does a toad hop or walk?

3. Who plays Carla Tortelli in *Cheers*?

4. *La dame de fer* is the nickname for which French attraction?

5. In which sport can you get 'three in a bed'?

6. What is the image in Jasper Johns' painting *Flag*?

7. What was the name of the gambling club in the Lord Lucan affair?

8. How many complete symphonies did Edward Elgar compose?

9. What is the UK's national bird?

10. What was Japan's former capital city?

11. In poker, what hand beats a straight flush?

12. What does the E stand for in 'E numbers'?

13. Whose autobiography was titled *Don't Laugh At Me*?

14. What BBC institution was built in 1932?

15. What is an homunculus?

16. Astrologically speaking, how is Margaret Anne Lake better known?

QUIZ 143

① Which US state's motto is 'North to the Future'?

② The Orange Fiction Award is limited to whom?

③ What is the medical term for drilling a hole in the skull?

④ Which Hungarian-born conductor was knighted in 1972?

⑤ Where is the spiritual home of Jack Daniels whiskey?

⑥ In which prison was Little Dorrit born?

⑦ In ancient Greece Demosthenes was famous as a what?

⑧ What is the framework of a dartboard known as?

⑨ Who was the leader of the Vietnamese nationalist movement?

⑩ What do Scots use a 'spurtle' for?

⑪ Who composed the opera *Prince Igor*?

⑫ What is a Bishop's Mitre when it isn't an item of headgear?

⑬ Which writer of dead cert thrillers died in 2010?

⑭ What does SKYPE stand for?

⑮ Who sang about 'Puppy Love' in 1972?

⑯ Who claimed: 'They misunderestimated me'?

QUIZ 144

① Who won the 2009 Nobel Peace Prize?

② What nationality was Albert Einstein?

③ In bingo, which number is 'The Lord is my shepherd'?

④ Which US president's vision was 'The Great Society'?

⑤ Who scored more England goals, Kevin Keegan or Alan Shearer?

⑥ Which familiar cuppa is named after a British statesman?

⑦ Who did Kofi Annan succeed as UN secretary-general?

⑧ Which Shakespeare play begins: 'Who's there?'?

⑨ Where is Master Sergeant Ernie Bilko based?

⑩ Who was the first British king to wear a kilt in public?

⑪ Who is the Greek god of dreams?

⑫ Who said: 'I am not young enough to know everything.'?

⑬ How is the 'Ant Bear' better known?

⑭ Who was Sid Vicious' girlfriend?

⑮ What is a grand slam in bridge?

⑯ Which Brontë was older, Charlotte or Emily?

QUIZ 145

① Who wrote the novel *Planet of the Apes*?

② Gordon Richards won The Derby in 1953 after how many attempts?

③ Who was awarded the Nobel Prize for Physics in 1921?

④ What is a ship's compass mounted on?

⑤ How many animals are there in the Chinese Zodiac?

⑥ Who said: 'I have never delivered a firebrand speech'?

⑦ What was Terry Wogan's devoted radio audience known as?

⑧ Who won seven gold medals at the 1972 Olympics?

⑨ Which UK Secretary of State for Education resigned in 2002?

⑩ What does the German phrase *ich dien* mean?

⑪ Who was the governor of Louisiana assassinated in 1935?

⑫ What is the world's lightest wood?

⑬ How old was Jimi Hendrix when he died in 1970?

⑭ What is the product name Spam derived from?

⑮ 'Farewell' is the last word of which iconic 17th-century novel?

⑯ What in southern Italy is the Camorra?

QUIZ 146

① How many funnels did the *Titanic* have?

② Which metal is the best conductor of electricity?

③ What is the only star sign not named after a living creature?

④ *The Rats* was whose first novel?

⑤ What is someone who provokes people into breaking the law?

⑥ What political party was the UK's first female Cabinet minister?

⑦ Who created the Russian Red Army?

⑧ What is Mozart's Symphony No 41 called?

⑨ Add the sporting surname: Gavin and Scott . . .

⑩ In the TV series, who was Cracker's long-suffering wife?

⑪ Which continent has the largest reserves of coal?

⑫ 'Pan Pan' signals what at sea?

⑬ Who was Charlemagne's vertically challenged father?

⑭ The Eagles were originally the backing group for which singer?

⑮ Which two brothers appear in the film *Good Will Hunting*?

⑯ Name the only British monarch of the House of Saxe-Coburg-Gotha.

QUIZ 147

① In which year was the Spanish flu pandemic?

② What is the name of Scarlett Johansson's twin brother?

③ Complete the proverb: A mackerel sky is never long . . .

④ What is a compound leaf of a fern or palm called?

⑤ Which French Revolutionary was murdered in his bath?

⑥ Charles de Ville Wells broke what in 1891?

⑦ What is the computer called in the TV series *Blake's 7*?

⑧ Who is the poet in Shakespeare's *Julius Caesar*?

⑨ What sporting item is an oxer?

⑩ Where is the headquarters of the Fleet Air Arm?

⑪ How is the disease *pertussis* more commonly known?

⑫ What was Percy Shelley's middle name?

⑬ Who is regarded as the founder of the quantum theory?

⑭ What was Status Quo's first and only No 1 hit single?

⑮ Which US state was founded first, Mississippi or Missouri?

⑯ What can be a fabric or a flower?

QUIZ 148

① In which country was Winston Churchill's mother born?

② Whose daughters are Rumer, Scout and Tallulah?

③ The Cheka was a secret police organization in which country?

④ Who won an Oscar for his song 'Streets of Philadelphia'?

⑤ Which particle in an atom has no electrical charge?

⑥ Who is the Hindu god of love?

⑦ What TV show is HIGNFY?

⑧ Which Caribbean island is less than 20 miles from Venezuela?

⑨ In heraldry, what colour is 'sanguine'?

⑩ What does the Old English word 'weald' mean?

⑪ Which Australian city is further north, Canberra or Perth?

⑫ Where did the game pelota originate?

⑬ What family of bird is the dunlin?

⑭ Which organization is BALPA?

⑮ What is the writer Ian Fleming's middle name?

⑯ Which hard-boiled US private eye calls his gun 'Betsy'?

QUIZ 149
CINEMA & TV

① Who does Laurence Fox play in the TV series *Lewis*?

② Peter Graves was which Western star's younger brother?

③ What are the rival gangs in *West Side Story*?

④ Actor Edward Norton is fluent in which foreign language?

⑤ Who was John Cleese's co-writer on *Fawlty Towers*?

⑥ In which 1995 film does Kevin Spacey play a serial killer?

⑦ Where was the cult series *The Prisoner* filmed?

⑧ Which 1930 anti-war film was remade in 1979?

⑨ Who is Bruce Willis' character in the *Die Hard* films?

⑩ Which two Scottish doctors shared Arden House?

⑪ Whose eight minutes on screen were enough for an Oscar in 1998?

⑫ Complete the film title: *Last Year at* . . .

⑬ Which US state is the background to *The Blair Witch Project*?

⑭ Who was the sleepy bunny of the *Magic Roundabout*?

⑮ Who leapt to fame in the film *Free Willy*?

⑯ Whose jazz band makes an unlikely appearance in *Blazing Saddles*?

QUIZ 150

① Who is Woody Harrelson's character in *Cheers*?

② What is the Caribbean island of Grenada also known as?

③ Who composed *The Tales of Hoffmann*?

④ What is a springtail?

⑤ Which US city boasts an Eiffel Tower?

⑥ What is the Italian word for confectionery?

⑦ Who refused his Oscar for 'Best Actor' in 1970?

⑧ Over how many days is a decathlon staged?

⑨ What are pollywogs?

⑩ The *czardas* is a dance of which country?

⑪ What do oologists study?

⑫ Which Celtic god is known as 'The Blessed'?

⑬ What was Roger Moore's first Bond film?

⑭ Who is the investigating monk in *The Name of the Rose*?

⑮ What is the currency of Uganda?

⑯ Which Donna Summer song did the BBC ban in 1976?

QUIZ 151

① What word can follow foot, hot or side?

② Name the Jolie-Pitt twins.

③ Who coined the phrase 'Sloane Ranger'?

④ What forbidding institution is in Ossining, New York?

⑤ Where in London do Steptoe and Son live?

⑥ Who wrote the play *An Enemy of the People*?

⑦ Who was the 2007 BBC Sports Personality of the Year?

⑧ How many ways can a batsman be given out in cricket?

⑨ Who was the third president of the USA?

⑩ What is the name of Mr Punch's dog?

⑪ What is a ginkgo: a currency, lizard or tree?

⑫ Which language is most spoken in Switzerland?

⑬ Who was lead vocal for The Four Tops?

⑭ What was the name of Leonardo DiCaprio's character in *Titanic*?

⑮ What is the collective name for dolphins?

⑯ In which year was the Berlin Airlift?

QUIZ 152

① Who was the mother of Oedipus?

② Which Brontë wrote *Wuthering Heights*?

③ What was the title of Take That's comeback album?

④ What is the setting for Jean-Paul Sartre's play *No Exit*?

⑤ Who is the patron saint of fathers?

⑥ In which year was the Aberfan disaster?

⑦ What is the currency of Afghanistan?

⑧ Which football referee invented red and yellow cards?

⑨ What is Scottish tablet?

⑩ Who discovered carbon dioxide in 1754?

⑪ What were Blurr previously called?

⑫ Who composed *The Dream of Gerontius*?

⑬ What is minus 459°F (to the nearest decimal point) called?

⑭ Whose follies went from Broadway to Hollywood?

⑮ In the New Testament, what is the Book of Acts' full title?

⑯ Who went courting as an eagle, a cloud and a shower of gold?

QUIZ 153

① Which dog saved Hollywood in a 1976 film?

② What was East Germany's state security ministry called?

③ British and US women golfers compete for which trophy?

④ How many kings apart were James I and James II?

⑤ What is a mound of stones covering a grave or tomb called?

⑥ Christ's Hospital school is also known as what?

⑦ Which organization did Reverend Chad Varah found in 1953?

⑧ Who starred in and directed the 1986 film *Under the Cherry Moon*?

⑨ What name is given to a wall made of unbaked clay and straw?

⑩ Which extreme right-wing group was founded in the USA in 1958?

⑪ What is Germany's most popular fruit loaf?

⑫ What was The Beatles' last UK No 1?

⑬ Dan Dare was a character in which children's comic?

⑭ What is the classification of living organisms into groups called?

⑮ What album was No 1 in the UK charts for the whole of 1959?

⑯ The poet Robert Burns was born in which part of Scotland?

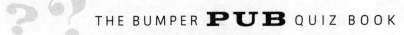

QUIZ 154

1) How many times did Muhammad Ali beat Joe Frazier?

2) What was the name of Haiti's notorious secret police?

3) Which film won Oscars in 2009 for best original score and song?

4) Hippolytus is the patron saint of what?

5) What is the Spanish parliament called?

6) For how many years was Margaret Thatcher prime minister?

7) What is Antarctica's highest mountain?

8) Who composed 'Zorba's Dance'?

9) Whose last words were: 'The rest is silence.'?

10) What flag in motor-racing indicates danger ahead, no overtaking?

11) Georges Feydeau is associated with which style of drama?

12) What was the name of the cat in the 1960s Spillers commercials?

13) Which 1985 film featured the song 'When The Going Gets Tough'?

14) Who was the wartime head of RAF Bomber Command?

15) In *Lord of the Rings*, which horse could only Gandalf ride?

16) What is the hole in a ship's bow through which the anchor chain passes?

QUIZ 155

① How many times was William Gladstone prime minister?

② Which US state borders Georgia to the west?

③ Which legendary lady's horse was called Aethenoth?

④ What is the provincial capital of Alberta in Canada?

⑤ In which year did the Ryder Cup begin?

⑥ Which 20th-century artist's last words were: 'Drink to me.'?

⑦ NINE THUMPS is an anagram of which word?

⑧ Which James Bond novel has the shortest title?

⑨ How many major islands make up the Azores?

⑩ From what part of Canada do Labrador dogs come?

⑪ Which Russian tsar murdered his own son?

⑫ What was the code name for the Dam Busters' bouncing bomb?

⑬ Which US state flag incorporates the Union Jack?

⑭ What headgear did New York's crime-fighter Guardian Angels wear?

⑮ What is the acting profession's trade union called?

⑯ What was the name of the Zionist terrorist group operating in Palestine until 1949?

QUIZ 156
SCIENCE & NATURE

① Which scientist wrote *The Blind Watchmaker*?

② What is the lay term for seasonal allergic rhinitis?

③ Which Greek mathematician wrote *The Elements*?

④ What is an Ishihara test used for?

⑤ What colour does the male stickleback turn when courting?

⑥ What is 0° Fahrenheit in centigrade?

⑦ What is the study of the flow of matter?

⑧ What is the UK's smallest bat?

⑨ Which part of the eye contains no blood vessels?

⑩ What do the computer letters MIPS stand for?

⑪ How many eyes do most species of spiders have?

⑫ What in the heavens is 2005 YU55?

⑬ What produces more fissile material than it consumes?

⑭ Muscology is a study of what vegetation?

⑮ The scolex is the front end of what parasite?

⑯ What are Agrippa, Proclus and Thales?

QUIZ 157

① Who played keyboard in the 1990s group D:Ream?

② How old was Guy Gibson when he led the RAF Dam Busters?

③ What is the world's oldest Sunday newspaper?

④ Which country includes the Isle of Tiree?

⑤ Where is the oldest public golf course in the USA?

⑥ What is Ben-Hur's first name?

⑦ How is K'ung Fu-tzu better known?

⑧ What does the expression 'to cross the Rubicon' mean?

⑨ What in 1950s Australia and New Zealand were bodgies and widgies?

⑩ Which famous English writer lived at Bateman's?

⑪ Who composed the album *Tubular Bells*?

⑫ Which tennis star was stabbed on court in 1993?

⑬ For which 1993 song did Tim Rice receive an Oscar?

⑭ Who plays Det. Jack Vincennes in the 1997 film *LA Confidential*?

⑮ Which is the smallest of the Five Great Lakes?

⑯ In the world of James Bond, what is Q's real name?

QUIZ 158

① How many kings separate Henry I from Edward I?

② Who composed the music for *Slumdog Millionaire*?

③ Why was the tennis player 'Gorgeous Gussie' Moran so called?

④ When was the Festival of Britain?

⑤ How many passenger capsules are there on the London Eye?

⑥ Who wrote the 16th-century philosophical work *Utopia*?

⑦ 'Menabilly' was which English writer's Cornish home?

⑧ Which UK jazz singer was born Clementina Dinah Campbell?

⑨ What woodpecker is bigger, the green or great spotted?

⑩ Whose pet Chihuahua has 'authored' its own memoirs?

⑪ Which European football club did Bobby Robson manage twice?

⑫ What was the title of North Korean leader Kim Il-sung?

⑬ In which South American country is Lake Poopó?

⑭ What was Colonel Gaddafi's home town?

⑮ What is a teasel?

⑯ Which iconic jazz singer was a former prostitute?

QUIZ 159

① Which word can follow brace, coup and gaunt?

② In which year was FIFA founded?

③ What coarse fabric is woven from jute or hemp?

④ *Semper fidelis* is the motto of which US fighting force?

⑤ What does *Semper fidelis* mean?

⑥ In which film is the leading character Dorothy Gale?

⑦ Who played tenor sax at his own London jazz club?

⑧ Which 'Brook' follows Beecher's in the Grand National?

⑨ Which liqueur is used in a Sidecar cocktail?

⑩ Whose name became a generic term for a traitor?

⑪ Where is the Gulf of Carpentaria?

⑫ Who is Inspector Clouseau's manservant?

⑬ Which instrument did jazz musician John Coltrane play?

⑭ If you are cyberphobic, what are you afraid of?

⑮ Which athlete's nickname was 'Flo-Jo'?

⑯ Which former SS officer was known as the 'Butcher of Lyons'?

QUIZ 160

① What is the smallest of the Balearic Islands?

② Tomáš Masaryk was the first president of which European country?

③ Where is the Uffizi gallery?

④ In the 1950s, which three singers recorded 'Singing The Blues'?

⑤ Which US film director was a master of hounds in Galway?

⑥ What activity is ikebana?

⑦ Who won the 2011 Tour de France?

⑧ What was author John Buchan's official title?

⑨ Who did Frank Sinatra christen 'Mr Mumbles'?

⑩ Where is the home of the Prime Meridian?

⑪ Who, in Polynesian mythology, was the first man?

⑫ What is the capital city of Nevada?

⑬ What are the drunken cousins of leprechauns called?

⑭ Who was the first international cricket match between?

⑮ Who composed the opera *Manon*?

⑯ In the world of fashion, what does *dernier cri* mean?

QUIZ 161

① What Yugoslavian city was destroyed by an earthquake in 1963?

② Which artist's other names were di Ludovico Buonarroti Simoni?

③ What is LASER short for?

④ Who shows Alice how to dance the Lobster Quadrille?

⑤ Add the showbiz surname: Babs, Joy and Teddy . . .

⑥ Which Egyptian pharaoh built the Temples of Abu Simbel?

⑦ Port Elizabeth is in which region of South Africa?

⑧ Who directed *The Dirty Dozen*?

⑨ Which Olympic event requires a plant box?

⑩ From which vegetable is tamari sauce made?

⑪ Who was born first, Peter Cook or Dudley Moore?

⑫ Which football guru was nicknamed 'Rabbi'?

⑬ Who conducts the orchestra in the Disney film *Fantasia*?

⑭ Broom Girl and Lord Kitchener are varieties of which fruit?

⑮ Eric Hobsbawm is one of Britain's foremost what?

⑯ Which former pop star and actor died suddenly in 2003?

QUIZ 162

① What does *ex cathedra* mean?

② Laurence Stephen are the first names of which 20th-century artist?

③ Who won the final of the first *Maestro* competition on TV?

④ What drug comes from the bark of the cinchona tree?

⑤ What precious stone celebrates a 45th wedding anniversary?

⑥ Malawi shares Lake Malawi with which two other countries?

⑦ What famous cricketer was born with an extra finger on each hand?

⑧ Who does King Arthur kill and is himself killed by?

⑨ How did the Norwegian explorer Roald Amundsen die?

⑩ What new service took off in Australia in 1928?

⑪ In which country was barley first grown?

⑫ In *Absolutely Fabulous*, what is Edina's surname?

⑬ What are Piccadilly Weepers?

⑭ How is Florian Cloud de Bounevialle Armstrong better known?

⑮ What is the southern tip of Manhattan Island called?

⑯ Who composed *Der Rosenkavalier*?

QUIZ 163

① Who created the world's biggest Ponzi scheme?

② Which UK anarchist group carried out bombings in the 1970s?

③ When ground what pigment does lapis lazuli produce?

④ Who scored the most Test runs: Weekes, Worrell or Walcott?

⑤ Where does a barista work?

⑥ Which is Africa's smallest mainland state?

⑦ In which European country were the first English-language newspapers printed?

⑧ Which 19th-century English poet died in a mental asylum?

⑨ With which 1990s band did Gwen Stefani perform?

⑩ Which ruling dynasty is most associated with Florence?

⑪ Add the Hollywood surname: Joan and John . . .

⑫ What does the Test cricket ground the WACA stand for?

⑬ What is a river otter's nest called?

⑭ Which sea lies between Sardinia and mainland Italy?

⑮ The archaeological site of Sutton Hoo is in which county?

⑯ Who plays General Worden in *The Dirty Dozen*?

QUIZ 164
MUSIC

① What R is Dolly Parton's middle name?

② Who was the first UK female singer to perform live behind the Iron Curtain?

③ And in which country did she perform?

④ How many artists got together for 'Do They Know It's Christmas'?

⑤ Which Beach Boys single was a traditional Caribbean tune?

⑥ Who wrote the music for the song 'Jerusalem'?

⑦ How is reggae singer Cecil Bustamente Campbell better known?

⑧ Which band's 2010 album was titled *Contra*?

⑨ Leona Lewis and Jesse J were classmates with which other singer?

⑩ Which US poet is the singer Mýa named after?

⑪ Who was the first male singer to win a BRIT award?

⑫ In which R&B group did Alesha Dixon perform?

⑬ Who teamed up with Mariah Carey for 'Endless Love'?

⑭ In which 1968 film is the song 'Windmills Of Your Mind'?

⑮ Which 17th-century Italian composer was nicknamed 'The Red Priest'?

⑯ How many people made up The Village People?

QUIZ 165

① Which US president's first names are James Earl?

② What is Walpurgis Night?

③ Which Pre-Columbian civilization came first, Inca or Mochica?

④ What is stored in the gall bladder?

⑤ *Madonna and Child* is the work of which British sculptor?

⑥ How old is a quinquagenarian?

⑦ In Disney's *Pocahontas*, whose voice is Captain John Smith's?

⑧ Where is the Ross Sea?

⑨ In which year was Chicago's St Valentine's Day Massacre?

⑩ What was the Japanese emperor called in olden days?

⑪ Helm is a strong wind associated with which part of the UK?

⑫ What bird features on the Sussex County Cricket Club badge?

⑬ And how many of them are there?

⑭ JAUNT is an anagram of what?

⑮ Which UK politician faked his death in Florida in 1974?

⑯ What was actress Sandra Bullock's mother's profession?

QUIZ 166

① Which English rebel was based in the Fens?

② Whose pen name was 'Q'?

③ Which strait connects the Pacific and Atlantic oceans?

④ What does the word acropolis mean?

⑤ Which is the oldest line on the London Underground?

⑥ Pannage is the rural right to do what?

⑦ How many legs does a woodlouse have?

⑧ Which ex-Liverpool goalkeeper was accused of match-fixing?

⑨ Which British territory became a dominion in 1907?

⑩ In which ocean is the island of Hispaniola?

⑪ Whose adopted son was named Bamm-Bamm?

⑫ What word means dirt, fungi and vulgarity?

⑬ What musical instrument is played by the wind?

⑭ What is the name of the pet raven in *Barnaby Rudge*?

⑮ Which airport do Doncaster and Sheffield share?

⑯ What did Nicolas-Jacques Conté invent in 1795?

QUIZ 167

① What does *carpe diem* mean?

② In Greek mythology, who killed the Minotaur?

③ What is France's equivalent of the Oscar?

④ Which two gulfs are linked by the Strait of Hormuz?

⑤ Who wrote the novel *The Ship of Fools*?

⑥ Who painted *The Ship of Fools*?

⑦ What can be part of an intestine or a punctuation mark?

⑧ What variety of tree is a hemlock?

⑨ The Oscar-winning 'When You Believe' was sung by which star duo?

⑩ Where was the first Test cricket match in England played?

⑪ In Japan do motorists drive on the left or right?

⑫ Who was MP Jeremy Thorpe cleared of attempting to murder in 1979?

⑬ A carrying yoke was normally made of which wood?

⑭ Whose brainchild was the mercury thermometer?

⑮ What is LJBF in Internet chat?

⑯ Which English cartoonist and satirist died in 1996?

QUIZ 168

① What word can follow aim, clue and point?

② Bulgaria, Romania and Georgia all border which sea?

③ What disease means 'bad air'?

④ Who founded the Missionaries of Charity in 1950?

⑤ What hat takes its name from a character in *Barnaby Rudge*?

⑥ Which singer/actor started life as Terry Nelhams?

⑦ Which mythological two-legged dragon had a rooster's head?

⑧ How long was the smash-hit 1903 movie *The Great Train Robbery*?

⑨ Which 18th-century novelist made a journalistic tour of Britain?

⑩ How many sides has a chiliagon?

⑪ The construction of Windsor Castle began under which king?

⑫ The Shining Path is a Maoist guerilla group in which country?

⑬ Which US statesman invented bifocals?

⑭ What Christmas song does Bill Nighy sing in *Love Actually*?

⑮ In which Chinese city was the Porcelain Tower?

⑯ What does pulchritude mean?

QUIZ 169

① In which year was the General Strike?

② Who was Chancellor of the Exchequer at the time?

③ What was Elvis Presley's 1957 Christmas song?

④ Who was the first boxer to beat Muhammad Ali?

⑤ What is Somerset's only city?

⑥ Who scored the only goal in the 2007 FA Cup final?

⑦ Which US president was a former director of the CIA?

⑧ What are the points on a deer's antlers called?

⑨ What eco-botanical endeavour was the brainchild of Tim Smit?

⑩ What is the Chinese parliament called?

⑪ In which city is W A Mozart airport?

⑫ How many toes does a zygodactyl bird have?

⑬ Thomas Hardy gave up a career as what to become a writer?

⑭ What type of wine is the legendary Château Yquem?

⑮ Who signed his paintings 'OK'?

⑯ Who quipped: 'For years I thought the club's name was Partick Thistle Nil.'?

QUIZ 170

① What is the German word for street?

② The rivers Bure, Waveney and Yare are in which English county?

③ To what family do cabbages and cauliflowers belong?

④ Flu-flu and Footed are types of what?

⑤ Who said: 'If the facts don't fit the theory, change the facts.'?

⑥ What is the video-game character Donkey Kong?

⑦ How many Grand Nationals did Red Rum run?

⑧ Which Scottish tribe built fortified homesteads called 'brochs'?

⑨ What penal colony was off the coast of French Guiana?

⑩ How many masts does a sloop have?

⑪ Whose debut solo album was titled *Faith*?

⑫ In which century did the Industrial Revolution begin?

⑬ In musical terms, what is a berceuse?

⑭ Which golfer's knighthood was announced after his death in 1987?

⑮ What was the prize in the Judgement of Paris?

⑯ John Everett Millais' painting 'Bubbles' was used to advertise which product?

QUIZ 171
HISTORY

① Who was the UK's first popular television historian?

② Who became Lord Protector of England in 1658?

③ Which US general said: 'War is hell'?

④ Whose record long reign did Queen Victoria overtake in 1896?

⑤ When was the 'Six Day' Arab-Israeli war?

⑥ Who was the first Protestant Archbishop of Canterbury?

⑦ Which Vietnamese village was the scene of a 1968 massacre?

⑧ Who became emperor of France in 1852?

⑨ Which saint started life as Giovanni di Bernardone?

⑩ Who is Britain's only illegitimate prime minister to date?

⑪ Of which English tribe was Queen Boadicea the ruler?

⑫ Who led the English to victory at Crécy and Poitiers?

⑬ Who was Blackbeard the pirate?

⑭ Which US president started the US Peace Corps?

⑮ Name the North Sea oil rig that sank in 1980 killing over 100 people.

⑯ Who was the instigator of the 1978 Jonestown massacre?

QUIZ 172

① In the TV series *Cracker*, who does Robbie Coltrane play?

② How many cathedrals are there in Liverpool?

③ Who was the weapons expert controversially found dead in 2003?

④ Ombrology is the study of what?

⑤ Who made a hit out of the 'Funky Gibbon' song?

⑥ The Kara Sea and the Laptev Sea are part of which ocean?

⑦ Alfred Hitchcock made how many films with Cary Grant?

⑧ Who captained Team Europe in the 2008 Ryder Cup?

⑨ Which US presidential address is given every January?

⑩ How old was Dylan Thomas when he died?

⑪ How many kilograms equal 1 tonne?

⑫ What was third time lucky for Ranulph Fiennes in 2009?

⑬ Which Egyptian goddess had the head of a cat?

⑭ An assassination attempt was made on which singer's life in 1976?

⑮ What is a single stone or pip in fruit called?

⑯ Which French rugby player won 118 Test caps?

QUIZ 173

1. What is the international dialling code for Poland?

2. In what part of the body do you find rods and cones?

3. Name the first man to win three consecutive Olympic boxing golds.

4. On what side of the road do Indonesians drive?

5. Which Greek deity equated with the Roman god Mercury?

6. What is Indian spinner Harbhajan Singh's nickname?

7. By which other name is the Great Indian Desert known?

8. Which group declared in 1979 'Video Killed The Radio Star'?

9. What fruit is distilled to make calvados?

10. Which flower's name comes from the French for 'lion's tooth'?

11. Where was Mary Queen of Scots executed?

12. What was unique about the 1973 rugby Five Nations?

13. In which opera do Ping, Pang and Pong appear?

14. What is a horizontal passage into a mine called?

15. Who succeeded John Betjeman as Poet Laureate in 1984?

16. Which Scottish football club is also a Walter Scott novel?

QUIZ 174

① Who was nicknamed the 'Chingford Skinhead'?

② What type of alphabet is the NATO alphabet?

③ Buzz Aldrin's mother's maiden name was Moon – true or false?

④ Who was the first bowler to take 400 Test wickets?

⑤ In which 1975 film is there a character called Homer Simpson?

⑥ And on whose novel was the film based?

⑦ Who is Shylock's daughter?

⑧ What bird is on Germany's coat of arms?

⑨ Who wrote the song 'Just Like A Woman'?

⑩ What are Kabbalists?

⑪ Who was the first Welsh rugby player to win 100 Test caps?

⑫ What do leprechauns do for a living?

⑬ Who was the oldest member of the Jackson Five?

⑭ What in 1968 became Africa's first Marxist state?

⑮ Whose catchphrase was: 'It's turned out nice again.'?

⑯ What is the wedge-shaped part of an anchor called?

QUIZ 175

① What terrorist group's name means 'The Base'?

② Mike Brearley captained England in how many Tests?

③ What heroic figure ruled Scotland for 20 years?

④ How many mounted umpires supervise a polo match?

⑤ What is the name of the country club in *The Archers*?

⑥ How is Sean John Combs better known?

⑦ Vexillology is the study of what?

⑧ What is a quetzal: a bird, a fish, or a snack food?

⑨ In what dance do you slap thighs, knees and soles of feet?

⑩ What film takes place on Skull Island?

⑪ Whose 2008 debut album *Rockferry* went to No 1?

⑫ What vegetable is a Solanum tuberosum?

⑬ What was the name of the Russian submarine that sank in 2000?

⑭ Which English poet wrote *The Pied Piper of Hamelin*?

⑮ Moving clockwise on a dartboard, what number is next to 1?

⑯ Which country's motto is 'From Sea to Sea'?

QUIZ 176

① What in Germany is a *bahnhof*?

② In which year did Nelson Mandela become South Africa's president?

③ Which Scottish novelist's first names are Alison Louise?

④ What nationality was racing driver Emerson Fittipaldi?

⑤ What was Saddam Hussein's political party?

⑥ Which UK prime minister introduced a 10.30pm TV curfew?

⑦ Who was Grateful Dead's lead vocalist?

⑧ What in Internet chat is HAND?

⑨ Who was unseeded when he won his first Wimbledon singles title?

⑩ Who directed the film *Casablanca*?

⑪ Fell, Dale and Connemara are breeds of which animal?

⑫ How was the English politician William Lamb better known?

⑬ What new life did the *QE2* take up in 2008?

⑭ Who designed a push-up bra for Jane Russell?

⑮ Which pop music entrepreneur was sent to jail in 2001?

⑯ Which Gus Van Sant film is based on Shakespeare's *Henry IV*?

QUIZ 177

① In which Welsh castle was Henry VII born?

② What word can come before bird, out and pool?

③ Who is Master and Commander?

④ When Led Zeppelin regrouped in 1988 who replaced John Bonham?

⑤ In the TV series *Mork and Mindy*, who played Mindy?

⑥ The gharial is a member of which reptilian family?

⑦ Who composed 'The Stars and Stripes Forever'?

⑧ What is Africa's biggest killer disease?

⑨ In which stately home was Winston Churchill born?

⑩ Who said: 'History is bunk.'?

⑪ W G Grace represented England at which other sport?

⑫ What is the name of the Scarlet Pimpernel?

⑬ Who was the first female US secretary of state?

⑭ What UK serial killer was known as the 'Black Panther'?

⑮ What are 'graupel'?

⑯ What is the collective noun for peacocks?

QUIZ 178

1. In which year did Channel 4 begin transmission?

2. What does KCVO stand for?

3. Which film star began life as Michael Shalhoub?

4. Which Australian cricket side was known as the 'Invincibles'?

5. In which year was the UK's first policewoman recruited?

6. What is the main circuit board of a computer called?

7. Who said: 'England is a nation of shopkeepers.'?

8. What does the Russian word *glasnost* mean?

9. How old was Mozart when he died?

10. Whose official country residence is Chevening House?

11. What followed *The Adventures of Tom Sawyer*?

12. Constantin Brancusi was famous in which art form?

13. Who did Manchester United pay £29.1m for in 2002?

14. Which country did the USA invade in 1994?

15. What is the shortest book in The Bible?

16. How many minutes are there in a week?

QUIZ 179
GEOGRAPHY

1. What is the capital of Papua New Guinea?

2. Robinson Crusoe Island lies off the coast of which country?

3. Which country surrounds San Marino?

4. What is the world's longest canal?

5. What name is given to a wide vertical crack in a rock face?

6. Which city is known in Welsh as Abertawe?

7. What links the Mediterranean Sea to the Atlantic Ocean?

8. On which river is Berlin?

9. What is the official language of Angola?

10. Which two countries share the Gobi Desert?

11. What is the highest capital city in the world?

12. West Papua is a province of which country?

13. Pulkovo airport serves which Russian city?

14. Fissure and central are types of what?

15. What is the currency of Haiti?

16. In which UK city is the River Wandle?

QUIZ 180

① In which English coastal town was Charles Dickens born?

② How old was Queen Anne when she died: 49, 59 or 69?

③ What in a castle was the garderobe?

④ A tarpon is a species of what?

⑤ Whose 1963 report led to the closure of many UK railway lines?

⑥ Who played in The Jam and Style Council before going solo?

⑦ Which Greek mythological creature was half man, half goat?

⑧ Add the showbiz surname: Luke and Owen . . .

⑨ What kind of fuel is used to power jet aircraft?

⑩ Which English war poet died on 4 November 1918?

⑪ Who did George Clooney play in *ER*?

⑫ Who is Margaret Drabble's novelist sister?

⑬ What profession was the 18th-century Humphry Repton?

⑭ Which drink was good 'Anytime, any place, anywhere'?

⑮ What came first, Mesolithic or Neolithic?

⑯ Which was the first football club to float on the London Stock Exchange?

QUIZ 181

① Who became world heavyweight boxing champion in 1962?

② Which leisure centre does Gordon Brittas manage?

③ In which year did Team Europe first contest the Ryder Cup?

④ What was the name of the Queen's first corgi?

⑤ Which US poet was married to fellow poet Ted Hughes?

⑥ Who composed the opera *The Bartered Bride*?

⑦ Where is the home of the National Fruit Collection?

⑧ Geminids and perseids are what kind of phenomena?

⑨ What nationality was the novelist Mordecai Richler?

⑩ What is the golfing term for going three under par on a hole?

⑪ With what illness was Steve Redgrave diagnosed in 1997?

⑫ Where were the first-ever Winter Olympics held?

⑬ Who was elected president of Poland in 1990?

⑭ Whose 1978 album was 9 years and 3 months in the UK charts?

⑮ What does the name Aldershot mean?

⑯ Which great composer taught both Mozart and Beethoven?

QUIZ 182

① Who was Ron Howard's character in *Happy Days*?

② Which English cathedral has a Nelson's Column?

③ Who was the Greek goddess of love?

④ And who was her Roman counterpart?

⑤ In which card game can you score 'one for his nob'?

⑥ What species of animal is a porcupine?

⑦ How many VCs were won at the Battle of Rourke's Drift?

⑧ What type of stories did Zane Grey write?

⑨ What is Brazil's most famous football stadium?

⑩ How many ballets did Tchaikovsky compose?

⑪ What triangle has three sides of different lengths?

⑫ What was Hercule Poirot's first case?

⑬ How long is an Olympic size swimming pool?

⑭ What do ants secrete as a deterrent?

⑮ What is the fossilized resin of pine trees?

⑯ Thailand's flag is made up of which three colours?

QUIZ 183

① In which novel does private eye Philip Marlowe first appear?

② What was Gary Lineker's last professional football club?

③ Which Tokyo bridge is lit up with different colours at night?

④ What is the hierarchical system for groups of animals called?

⑤ In which war was the first Victoria Cross awarded?

⑥ What was Gareth Gates' 2002 No 1?

⑦ During whose reign was the House of Windsor created?

⑧ At which end of a cathedral is the choir, east or west?

⑨ Which tennis star was nicknamed the 'Rockhampton Rocket'?

⑩ What is the international calling code for Greece?

⑪ When was the first parachute jump made: 1783, 1793 or 1803?

⑫ 'Pops' was one of his nicknames – what was the other?

⑬ What was the first capital of Norway?

⑭ Atticus Finch is the hero of which American novel and film?

⑮ What is the home of the Irish Grand National?

⑯ The Battle of Waterloo was fought in which month of 1815?

QUIZ 184

① In *Little Britain*, who runs the fat-fighting class?

② Which English cathedral has the largest monastic cloister?

③ What was the first European nation to give women the vote?

④ What colour is 'verdant'?

⑤ Where is the San Siro Stadium?

⑥ Who was South Africa's second post-apartheid president?

⑦ Which instrument did Glenn Miller play?

⑧ On which English canal is the Blisworth Tunnel?

⑨ What does the Russian word *sputnik* mean?

⑩ Which land creature has the biggest eyes?

⑪ What children's classic did Antoine de Saint-Exupéry write?

⑫ Which US actor was awarded the *Légion d'honneur* in 2007?

⑬ Is a blenny a fish or a flower?

⑭ How is actor Sir John Leon better known?

⑮ Whose motto is *Dieu et mon droit*?

⑯ What was the world's first purpose-built motor-racing circuit?

QUIZ 185

① What three flavours make up Neapolitan ice cream?

② Ophelia and Cordelia are satellites of which planet?

③ Which film featured the single 'Vogue' by Madonna?

④ What did Nelson Mandela and F W de Klerke share in 1993?

⑤ Which English novelist coined the phrase 'corridors of power'?

⑥ What item of clothing are *zori*?

⑦ Who had a 1980s No 1 with 'Move Closer'?

⑧ Which English children's author married Trotsky's secretary?

⑨ Who in 2003 was voted Britain's 'Pipe Smoker of the Year'?

⑩ What can be a type of cake or a sail?

⑪ Who is the 'salesman' in Arthur Miller's play?

⑫ What fruit is associated with Bournemouth FC?

⑬ In which soap did Andrew Lloyd-Webber play himself in 2008?

⑭ What kind of creature is a crown-of-thorns?

⑮ What Test cricket ground is reduced to 'The Gabba'?

⑯ Which Tibetan mountain is sacred to five religions?

QUIZ 186
SPORT

① Who won the 1991 Rugby World Cup?

② Which is the oldest of the British horse-racing Classics?

③ Who was knighted in 1937 for his services to cricket?

④ How old was swimmer Michael Phelps at his first Olympics?

⑤ Who was the last Englishman to manage Chelsea?

⑥ What cycle race is the RAAM?

⑦ Which club had the first all-seater football stadium in England?

⑧ Which German Grand Prix circuit alternates with Nürburgring?

⑨ In which sport might you throw a 'buttonhook'?

⑩ Which golf course is called 'Scotland's Pebble Beach'?

⑪ What is the outer circle of the wrestling mat called?

⑫ Who won rugby league's Four Nations championship in 2010?

⑬ The Eisenhower Trophy is competed for in which sport?

⑭ Who did Mark Taylor follow as Australia's Test captain?

⑮ How old was Archie Moore when he fought Cassius Clay in 1962?

⑯ Add the sporting surname: Alex and Darren . . .

QUIZ 187

① What health benefit does plant stanols and sterols have?

② *Do Androids Dream of Electric Sheep?* became which film?

③ The Point of Ayre is on which UK island?

④ Which is the superior saffron, red or yellow?

⑤ Add the sporting surname: Albie and Morne . . .

⑥ Who won both a BAFTA and an Oscar for 'Best Actor' in 2008?

⑦ What is a fake cockney accent called?

⑧ Who wrote the poem 'I Wish I'd Looked After Me Teeth'?

⑨ Carly Simon's 1972 hit 'You're So Vain' is dedicated to whom?

⑩ In which year was Channel 5 launched?

⑪ Who composed the opera *Julius Caesar in Egypt*?

⑫ What type of dog is a Pomeranian?

⑬ How many days of fasting are there at Ramadan?

⑭ What is the Gaelic name for Scotland?

⑮ Which sport featured in the film *Any Given Sunday*?

⑯ What was John Lennon's middle name?

QUIZ 188

① What confectionery items are coloured chocolate oblate spheroids?

② A bourne is another name for what?

③ What is the native religion of Japan?

④ Which 18th-century 'royal' is lampooned in a nursery rhyme?

⑤ When did the Grammy Awards begin: 1948, 1953 or 1958?

⑥ Kelp is a major source of which mineral?

⑦ Which famous gambler is known as 'The Great Wall of China'?

⑧ Whose TV BAFTA nomination in 2007 was for a record 12th time?

⑨ By 2012 London will have hosted how many Olympic Games?

⑩ Which Australian cricket captain was a plumber by trade?

⑪ Who was lead singer for Ultravox?

⑫ What does NAS stand for?

⑬ Who painted *Rain, Steam and Speed: The Great Western Railway*?

⑭ Which Doyle designed the original cover for *Punch* magazine?

⑮ What is the male red grouse called?

⑯ Which fictional detective received a full-page obituary in the *New York Times* in 1975?

QUIZ 189

① Who became the Earl of Beaconsfield in 1876?

② Bath, Fiddleback and No 14 are all names of what?

③ In which British soap did Alvin Stardust play a pub landlord?

④ What can be a stage or a protective garment?

⑤ Which US-born writer lived at Lamb House in Rye?

⑥ In 1862 George Peabody set up a charitable trust to create what?

⑦ Who was Duran Duran's drummer?

⑧ Was Skippy the Bush Kangaroo male or female?

⑨ What flightless bird belongs to the *Spheniscidae* family?

⑩ Whose catchphrase was: 'I wanna tell you a story.'?

⑪ Where did John Bunyan begin writing *The Pilgrim's Progress*?

⑫ Who in the Bible is 'Lord of the Flies'?

⑬ Which heroic British general died at the 1809 Battle of Corunna?

⑭ Who founded the Littlewoods empire?

⑮ Who picked up three awards at the 2010 BRITS?

⑯ A 'knobber' is a young what?

QUIZ 190

① What is a musical composition for nine instruments?

② Who drinks Duff beer?

③ In the original novel, what is Dr Frankenstein's first name?

④ Whose newspaper is *The War Cry*?

⑤ Which composer's first names were Pyotr Ilyich?

⑥ What is a female alligator called?

⑦ Which group's first seven singles all went to No 1 in the UK?

⑧ Who directed the documentary *Bowling for Columbine*?

⑨ On which river is the city of Brazzaville?

⑩ What can be a flower or a butterfly?

⑪ Who was the first batsman to score 10,000 runs in Test cricket?

⑫ What was the first Stephen King book to be a film?

⑬ The Fields Medal is awarded for the highest achievement in what?

⑭ The herb liqueur Izarra comes from which part of Europe?

⑮ In which century was the Italian painter Caravaggio born?

⑯ Which Scottish poet wrote the words of 'Rule, Britannia!'?

QUIZ 191

① Who was born Piers Stefan O'Meara?

② Which temperature has the same value in Fahrenheit and Celsius?

③ Which famous UK literary couple married in 1980?

④ How many Foster brothers played cricket for Worcestershire?

⑤ What instrument did Miles Davis play?

⑥ In which series of films is Lt Ellen Ripley a character?

⑦ Where in the USA is Columbia University?

⑧ Who was the *Daily Mirror* agony aunt who died in 1996?

⑨ Horse races over fences or hurdles are called what?

⑩ With which branch of medical science was R D Laing associated?

⑪ Who is the Hindu god of lust and desire?

⑫ In which year did Steve Redgrave win his first Olympic gold?

⑬ What job did Harry Clayton do in *Coronation Street*?

⑭ Which English cricketer's first names were Charles Burgess?

⑮ In which European capital is the Charles Bridge?

⑯ Which Brontë wrote *The Tenant of Wildfell Hall*?

QUIZ 192

① What is a two-wheeled, self-balancing transportation machine?

② Which famous rock band was once called The High Numbers?

③ What is a female donkey called?

④ Which saint's name is linked to a neurological disease?

⑤ Name the hit song recorded by Glenn Hoddle and Chris Waddle.

⑥ Which British PM crops up in the 2004 novel *The Line of Beauty*?

⑦ In which year was the Indian Mutiny?

⑧ What is the Japanese word for 'goodbye'?

⑨ How much did the first TV licence cost?

⑩ Which painter had the surname Van Rijn?

⑪ Who plays Mrs Banks in the film *Mary Poppins*?

⑫ In Greek mythology, who was 'Mother Earth'?

⑬ Which is the last chemical element, in alphabetical order?

⑭ What did Sir Francis Drake call the Pacific coast of America?

⑮ Who wrote the lyrics for the song 'Hakuna Matata'?

⑯ Which BBC Director-General was the brother of a famous writer?

QUIZ 193

① In which country are the ruins of Troy?

② What was the name of Jane Austen's only sister?

③ What three-letter word can come before king, rage and row?

④ Who was the last English monarch killed in battle?

⑤ In which year did Concorde make its maiden flight?

⑥ What is the annual census of swans on the Thames called?

⑦ Who composed *The Love For Three Oranges*?

⑧ What did the outmoded TELEX stand for?

⑨ How many tennis tournaments make up the Grand Slam?

⑩ Who founded the *Daily Mail* in 1896?

⑪ What is a 'hirsel'?

⑫ Who lost to IBM's Deep Blue computer at chess in 1997?

⑬ What bird is sometimes called the 'pharaoh's chicken'?

⑭ Which children's author was born in Chipping Sodbury in 1965?

⑮ What did Erik Weisz magically change his name to?

⑯ Who won the men's football gold medal at the Beijing Olympics?

QUIZ 194
CINEMA & TV

① Which 1950 film received a record 14 Oscar nominations?

② And how many did it win?

③ Tim Canterbury is a character in which UK comedy series?

④ Which fraternal movie directors produce the TV series *Numb3rs*?

⑤ Who plays Sam in the 1942 film *Casablanca*?

⑥ Which TV chef was once half of the musical *Calypso Twins*?

⑦ Name the canine in the space-age cartoon series *The Jetsons*.

⑧ Who became the first chairman of BAFTA in 1947?

⑨ Which British sitcom was remade in the US as *Three's Company*?

⑩ Who did Christopher Eccleston succeed as Dr Who?

⑪ In the 1973 cartoon version of *Robin Hood* what animal was Robin?

⑫ Which novel was the inspiration for *Apocalypse Now*?

⑬ Robert De Niro made his directorial debut with which film?

⑭ Who played Paul McCartney's grandad in *A Hard Day's Night*?

⑮ Which 1940s Hollywood star became a Manhattan barmaid?

⑯ Which four Oscar-winning Aussies appeared on postage stamps?

QUIZ 195

① Who was Dwight Eisenhower's presidential running mate in 1952?

② In which children's TV series did Dennis Waterman make his name?

③ Who broke Bjorn Borg's championship run at Wimbledon in 1981?

④ Complete the proverb: 'A tale twice told is a cabbage . . .'

⑤ What was the Czech composer Smetena's first name?

⑥ Who moved from Juventus to Real Madrid for £45.62m in 2001?

⑦ What does the Japanese word *karaoke* mean?

⑧ What island is the 'Pearl of the Indian Ocean'?

⑨ Mother Shipton was a 16th-century what?

⑩ Who was Radio 1's first female DJ?

⑪ What was the name of the world's largest airship?

⑫ Archery is the national sport of which country?

⑬ Who hosted UK television's first dedicated fashion programme?

⑭ What colour is 'mazarine'?

⑮ Who wrote the novel *Madame Bovary*?

⑯ What is a bird of prey and something that flies in the wind?

QUIZ 196

① Which US star plays a Japanese character in the film *Sayonara*?

② The crew of which Russian ship famously mutinied in 1905?

③ Where is Los Rodeos airport?

④ In *Gulliver's Travels*, what is Gulliver's first name?

⑤ What type of aircraft was the Sunderland?

⑥ On what side of the road do they drive on in Nepal?

⑦ Who was FIFA's first World Player of the Year in 1991?

⑧ Which of the Marx Brothers was born Herbert Manfred Marx?

⑨ Nubia was a region alongside which African river?

⑩ In the 60s group The Dave Clark Five, what did Dave Clark play?

⑪ Which US football team is known as the '49ers'?

⑫ In R L Stevenson's story, what is Dr Jekyll's first name?

⑬ What is a horse that hasn't yet won a race called?

⑭ In the Bible, who was Noah's youngest son?

⑮ Who was the first person to sail solo around the world?

⑯ Where exactly did Renée Zellweger marry singer Kenny Chesney?

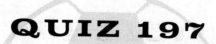

QUIZ 197

① Who was the leader of the Gunpowder plot?

② In which university city is the Dragon School?

③ What secures a saddle to a horse?

④ To which 1960s group did the poet Roger McGough belong?

⑤ What is the coloured shirt worn by a jockey called?

⑥ In which Russian novel is Raskolnikov the central character?

⑦ Which bird feigns injury to deceive potential predators of its young?

⑧ Dutch Warmblood and Russian Don are breeds of what animal?

⑨ Who was the wife of Agamemnon, mythical king of Mycenae?

⑩ Which ex-Australian Test cricketer published a cookbook in 2004?

⑪ What is the largest of the royal parks?

⑫ For which football team did the Greenhoff brothers play?

⑬ Which chatty TV family has guests round at 'No 42'?

⑭ In which year was the sound barrier first broken?

⑮ And who was the first pilot to do it?

⑯ Who was Frankie Goes to Hollywood's lead singer?

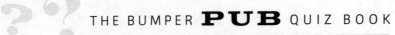

QUIZ 198

① What is a tropical flower and a filling for cakes?

② The Ten Commandments are in which book of the Bible?

③ Who wrote the Jemima Shore mysteries?

④ Which Yiddish word means shameless audacity or cheek?

⑤ Which 70s rock band had a hit with 'Good Morning Judge'?

⑥ What is a fletcher?

⑦ And who is their patron saint?

⑧ Who wrote the poem 'The Rape of the Lock'?

⑨ Which was the first to have a female cox, Oxford or Cambridge?

⑩ Who made the first solo balloon flight around the world?

⑪ How old was Princess Margaret when she died?

⑫ What is a passionate expression of grief?

⑬ Which super hero is Billy Batson's alter ego?

⑭ William Hogarth's *A Rake's Progress* comprises how many paintings?

⑮ What is the capital of Brazil?

⑯ A raglan is which part of a garment?

QUIZ 199

① What is the UK 'City of a Thousand Trades'?

② Playwright Lillian Hellman was married to which fellow author?

③ What is a scaphoid fracture?

④ The first bananas arrived in England in which century?

⑤ Where was the explorer Ernest Shackleton born?

⑥ What was the Eastern bloc equivalent of NATO?

⑦ The flag of Monaco is identical to which other country's flag?

⑧ How many singles rubbers are there in a Davis Cup match?

⑨ Which Roman general defeated Spartacus?

⑩ How did the 19th-century murderer William Palmer kill his victims?

⑪ Which word can follow fort, mid and over?

⑫ What are curling stones made of?

⑬ Who played Alf Garnett's wife in *Till Death Us Do Part*?

⑭ Which cricketer's 2008 memoirs were called *Coming Back to Me*?

⑮ 'I Need To Wake Up' was the wake-up call in which film?

⑯ In Botticelli's *The Birth of Venus*, what is Venus standing in?

QUIZ 200

① Apart from the obvious, what is a bottle brush?

② Which Englishman was a co-founder of United Artists?

③ Who was 'Jones the Steam'?

④ Which Titian masterpiece was saved for the nation in 2009?

⑤ Where in Scotland is Dyce Airport?

⑥ Between which two rivers was Mesopotamia?

⑦ In which US state is the village of Sleepy Hollow?

⑧ Who wrote the play *The Killing of Sister George*?

⑨ The original Olympic games were in honour of whom?

⑩ In which year did Radio 1 first go on air?

⑪ Who sang the theme song from the Bond movie *Licence to Kill*?

⑫ Which English poet wrote *Goldilocks and the Three Bears*?

⑬ Which is further north, Nanjing or Shanghai?

⑭ How does Marshall Bruce Mathers III prefer to be known?

⑮ Who won the Boat Race in 2010?

⑯ Who leads prayers in a mosque?

QUIZ 201
SCIENCE & NATURE

① What is the collective noun for jellyfish?

② In Maths, how many boundaries are there on a Möbius strip?

③ Is a shark a fish or a mammal?

④ What is the favoured food of the bird *Merops apiaster*?

⑤ Which dinosaur had the longest tail?

⑥ In which county is the Jodrell Bank Observatory?

⑦ What is an African Moon?

⑧ The word atom stems from the Greek *atomos*, meaning what?

⑨ What describes the airflow over moving objects?

⑩ In what part of the human body is the 'Island of Riel'?

⑪ What was the first to be delivered in 1978?

⑫ What does the Mohs Scale measure?

⑬ Which island did the dodo originally inhabit?

⑭ Monophobia is the fear of what?

⑮ Which plant produces the heart stimulant digitalis?

⑯ What is the popular name for the Pleiades group of stars?

QUIZ 202

① Where in England is the Baltic Centre for Contemporary Art?

② Which British bird became extinct in 1844?

③ Name the first batsman to score 200 in a one-day international.

④ Who does Humphrey Bogart play in *The Caine Mutiny*?

⑤ In which river is Eel Pie Island?

⑥ What can be a flower or a medicinal ingredient?

⑦ Which pop duo are Alison Mosshart and Jamie Hince?

⑧ Who said: 'The bigger they come, the harder they fall'?

⑨ What Indian city was the scene of a British-led massacre in 1919?

⑩ Who commanded the Continental Army in 1775?

⑪ Which 19th-century writer's middle name is Makepeace?

⑫ What is the highest mountain in Europe?

⑬ Princeton University is in which US state?

⑭ Who composed *The Three-Cornered Hat*?

⑮ What was Princess Margaret's favourite holiday destination?

⑯ In which 1980 film did Steven Spielberg make a guest appearance?

QUIZ 203

① How is the fish-hawk more commonly known?

② Who was the founder of Surrealism?

③ In which year was The Prince's Trust founded?

④ With what name did Cliff Richard start life?

⑤ Who was Germany's first post-war chancellor?

⑥ ColoRouge is a cheese of which country?

⑦ Who was the first monarch to reside at Buckingham Palace?

⑧ What is a male badger called?

⑨ Malt whisky is made from which two ingredients?

⑩ Which athlete became MP for Lewisham North in 1959?

⑪ What is a *bon mot*?

⑫ When was the Football World Cup first televised?

⑬ Who was the first of many to record 'The Christmas Waltz'?

⑭ Which is the world's second highest mountain?

⑮ Who was the novelist wife of Kingsley Amis?

⑯ All the royalties from *Peter Pan* go to which institution?

QUIZ 204

① What can be a means of conveyance or a burial mound?

② In which country was the sculptor Jacob Epstein born?

③ What variety of flower is the goldilock?

④ Which presidential wife was an obsessive collector of shoes?

⑤ In which country was Che Guevara killed?

⑥ Who won the 2008 US Masters?

⑦ Which 1960s pop group had a flautist up front?

⑧ What was the first UK club to win the European Champions Cup?

⑨ Who was the US commander at the Battle of Cassino?

⑩ Ace inhibitors are used to treat what medical condition?

⑪ What is the capital of Corsica?

⑫ Is a barbel a marine or freshwater fish?

⑬ Which Dostoevsky novel has a fraternal theme?

⑭ Which sister ship of the *Titanic* hit a mine and sank in 1916?

⑮ Which holder of the Victoria Cross devoted himself to charity?

⑯ Who said: 'Forgive your enemies, but never forget their names'?

QUIZ 205

① In which sport is a beamer illegal?

② In the Great War who were the VADs?

③ Dr Lydgate is a character in which George Eliot novel?

④ Who played the title role in the film *Shirley Valentine*?

⑤ Which British cyclist died during the 1967 Tour de France?

⑥ Verona is in which region of Italy?

⑦ What international sporting body is the ATP?

⑧ Who was elected US president in 1920?

⑨ What was U2's only UK No 1 single in the 1980s?

⑩ In which card game can players 'advertise'?

⑪ Which Scottish king was the hero at Bannockburn in 1314?

⑫ The title of H Rider Haggard's novel *She* is short for what?

⑬ Which Balkan country is Crna Gora in its own language?

⑭ At which European film festival is the 'Golden Swan' awarded?

⑮ Actor Charles Laughton was born in which Yorkshire town?

⑯ In the Arthurian legend, who was Sir Galahad's father?

QUIZ 206

① To which family of birds does the blackbird belong?

② What followed Milton's *Paradise Lost*?

③ Where was racing driver Ayrton Senna killed in 1994?

④ Whose 'midnight ride' in 1775 alerted the American rebels?

⑤ In which country is the Bay of Islands?

⑥ Which ancient vase did Josiah Wedgwood recreate in 1790?

⑦ Who was the first labour Member of Parliament?

⑧ Where in London was there a major rail crash in 1957?

⑨ Which Bristol-born artist sang about being a 'Wide Boy'?

⑩ Selma Lagerlöf was the first female winner of which Nobel prize?

⑪ Which rugby player's nickname was 'Bumface'?

⑫ What nationality was the astronomer Nicolaus Copernicus?

⑬ By what name was the Greek god Dionysus known to the Romans?

⑭ What was Moldova previously called?

⑮ On which peninsula is the Mayan city of Chichén Itzá?

⑯ What are the small celestial bodies that revolve around the sun?

QUIZ 207

1. In which book is the character Slartibartfast?

2. What was artist Andy Warhol's studio called?

3. Who was the first US president to win the Nobel Peace Prize?

4. Who painted *The Laughing Cavalier*?

5. In what guards regiment did Tommy Cooper serve in World War Two?

6. Which rock star was once William Perks?

7. Over what length is The Epsom Derby run?

8. What is Mount Stromboli?

9. Which European nation's flag is white with a blue cross?

10. What is a peruke?

11. Who sang the title song of the film *For Your Eyes Only*?

12. In which sport do you peg out?

13. Add the showbiz surname: Michelle and Dedee . . .

14. In Shakespeare's play *As You Like It*, what is Touchstone?

15. On a dartboard, what number is opposite 19?

16. In heraldry what shape is a lozenge?

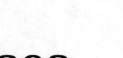

QUIZ 208
MUSIC

① In the opera of the same name, what is Tosca's profession?

② What nationality are Bloc Party?

③ In which film did Elvis Presley play a boxer?

④ What was Adele's 2011 platinum album called?

⑤ Which two 'brothers' won a BRIT in 2000?

⑥ What is the musical term for unaccompanied singers?

⑦ Who had a seasonal hit with 'Happy Christmas (War Is Over)'?

⑧ Which 18th-century composer wrote more than 100 symphonies?

⑨ Who noted 'The Times They Are A-Changing'?

⑩ What was Oasis called before 1991?

⑪ Who interrupted Michael Jackson's performance at the 1996 BRITS?

⑫ How did the singer Aaliyah die in 2001?

⑬ Complete the song title: 'I've Never Seen A Straight . . .'

⑭ Who sang the theme song for the Bond film *Thunderball*?

⑮ How is French pianist Philippe Pagès better known?

⑯ What ageless song did Mildred and Patty Hill write in 1893?

QUIZ 209

① Who in 2011 hosted the first 'Comedy Prom'?

② Who became the undisputed world chess champion in 2006?

③ In which game are there bamboos, dragons and flowers?

④ Which US state is nicknamed the 'Mother of Presidents'?

⑤ What is the only country bordering Denmark?

⑥ In which UK city is the Met Office headquarters?

⑦ Which Greek god was known as the 'Earthshaker'?

⑧ Which country singer was born Eilleen Regina Edwards?

⑨ Meadow, Wood and Slave-making are varieties of British what?

⑩ In *Happy Days* what was the 'Fonz's' first name?

⑪ Sir Anthony Caro is a well known what?

⑫ In London's Soho Square there is a statue of which English king?

⑬ Who was the bespectacled singer who wanted to 'Kiss The Bride'?

⑭ What is the world's smallest island nation?

⑮ Who painted *The Kiss*?

⑯ Who was Britain's first minister of the arts?

QUIZ 210

① Who won the FIFA Women's World Cup in 2011?

② To what family of birds do puffins and razorbills belong?

③ Who launched a 'Clean Up TV' campaign in 1965?

④ In the TV soap *Dallas*, what did J R Ewing's initials stand for?

⑤ Who wrote *The Decline and Fall of the Roman Empire*?

⑥ On which river is Boston, Lincolnshire?

⑦ On which river is Boston, Massachusetts?

⑧ How many pawns in a chess set?

⑨ What are you afraid of if you are dendrophobic?

⑩ Who for 40 years was the BBC's 'voice of tennis'?

⑪ Which actor had a hit in 1977 with 'Don't Give Up On Us'?

⑫ Nuku'alofa is the capital of where?

⑬ In the world of music, what is a machete?

⑭ What was Dan short for in US vice-president Dan Quayle?

⑮ Which UK national daily newspaper was founded in 1855?

⑯ Who was the second man to run a mile in under four minutes?

QUIZ 211

① What is Britain's flashiest bird?

② Who was the oldest of the Kennedy brothers?

③ Which Indian writer won the Nobel Literature Prize in 1913?

④ How is a cardinal addressed?

⑤ What arms limitation treaty did the US and USSR sign in 1979?

⑥ What is the electronic service monitor at Wimbledon called?

⑦ In which year did the Millennium Stadium open?

⑧ On which island is Tokyo situated?

⑨ Which technological pioneer died in 2011?

⑩ La Goulue was which French artist's most celebrated model?

⑪ Ursine describes which type of animal?

⑫ Was George W Bush left- or right-handed?

⑬ In heraldry, what colour is 'sable'?

⑭ Aqaba is which country's only port?

⑮ The musical *Guys and Dolls* is based on whose short stories?

⑯ What was Elvis Presley's rendition of 'O Sole Mio' called?

QUIZ 212

① What candid TV presenter died in 2008?

② Which of the Pet Shop Boys does most of the singing?

③ What does the phrase *sub rosa* mean?

④ Whose first novel *Beauty* won a 2009 Whitbread Prize?

⑤ In cockney rhyming slang, what is 'garden gate'?

⑥ What common British bird is a *Pica pica*?

⑦ Which admiral was blown up at sea by the IRA in 1979?

⑧ In which UK city is the Belgrade Theatre?

⑨ How many times did actor Henry Fonda marry?

⑩ What is the highest peak in the Pennines?

⑪ On what part of a ship would you find the futtock plates?

⑫ Where in London were the 1948 Olympics staged?

⑬ Who had a 1995 hit with 'One Hot Minute'?

⑭ Which Mary was a Welsh singer-songwriter?

⑮ Who wrote *Cold Comfort Farm*?

⑯ Which US president phoned Neil Armstrong on the moon?

QUIZ 213

① What relation is Mike Tindall to the Queen?

② In Victorian times what were 'Crushers'?

③ What is a *paterfamilias*?

④ Who was the 'Father of the Typewriter'?

⑤ What was the last Olympic Games before World War Two?

⑥ Which make of car was the Stingray or Corvette?

⑦ *Ally Sloper's Half Holiday* was the first British what?

⑧ What are the names of England's rugby Armitage brothers?

⑨ Which element has the highest melting point?

⑩ Who composed the theme music for TV's *Inspector Morse*?

⑪ Which US architect was noted for his 'prairie style' designs?

⑫ How many symphonies did Gustav Mahler compose?

⑬ Who was known as 'The Singing Brakeman'?

⑭ In *Keeping Up Appearances* what is the name of the Buckets' son?

⑮ What especially is sold at Bampton Fair in Devon?

⑯ Who was the yellow canary in the *Looney Tunes* cartoons?

QUIZ 214

① In which English county are the Wookey Hole caves?

② Which 19th-century English poet's spaniel was called Flush?

③ What do the initials stand for in the African political party ZANU-PF?

④ Whose 1964 'art' book was titled *Grapefruit*?

⑤ What are spectacles without earpieces called?

⑥ Which English actor has a one-man show as Charles Dickens?

⑦ What was ABBA's first UK No 1 single?

⑧ How many of the Orkney islands are inhabited?

⑨ The slow worm is what species of animal?

⑩ What is the only planet without a mythological name?

⑪ Who said: 'The medium is the message'?

⑫ What was the former name of Queens Park Rangers FC?

⑬ Which Spanish artist painted the Duke of Wellington?

⑭ Where will you find the ancient ruins of Carthage?

⑮ Richard Avedon was an artist in what field?

⑯ How old was Maureen Connelly when she won the Wimbledon Women's Singles title in 1952?

QUIZ 215

① Where in the Middle East is the 'Golden City'?

② Whose book *War Horse* has become a theatrical hit?

③ What is a tetrapod?

④ Who coined the phrase the 'unacceptable face of capitalism'?

⑤ Where would Victorian ladies have worn 'luggers'?

⑥ In which 1960s song does someone 'leave a cake out in the rain'?

⑦ What are the German international TV and Media awards called?

⑧ In which sport was Britain's Johnny Leach a world champion?

⑨ Who took over from his brother as president of Cuba in 2008?

⑩ In police jargon, what does DIP stand for?

⑪ What is the chemical symbol for tin?

⑫ What word can be something to eat with or a piano piece?

⑬ What was Goldfinger's first name?

⑭ LLD stands for what?

⑮ What is the English horn more generally known as?

⑯ Inigo Jones is identified with which style of architecture?

QUIZ 216
HISTORY

① Which war involving Britain lasted from 1948 to 1960?

② Who was Napoleon Bonaparte's second wife?

③ Which was the first republic in Western Europe?

④ What was introduced in the UK in 1991 to improve public standards?

⑤ When was NATO founded?

⑥ How old was James Callaghan when he died?

⑦ Who did Colonel Gaddafi overthrow in 1969?

⑧ Which Scottish king was killed in 1057?

⑨ When did the Californian Gold Rush begin?

⑩ Who did Nathuram Godse assassinate in 1948?

⑪ Which Marxist became president of Chile in 1970?

⑫ Who captured Quebec in 1759 and died in the process?

⑬ Who succeeded David Steel as leader of the Lib-Dems in 1988?

⑭ Who was Tsar Nicholas II's youngest daughter?

⑮ Who became Saudi Arabia's first king in 1932?

⑯ Which reforming Chinese leader died in 1997?

QUIZ 217

① What is the name of the Spider-Man musical?

② And who wrote the music and lyrics?

③ How was Cnut the Great otherwise known?

④ In bingo, what number is 'duck and dive'?

⑤ The Beatles made their first live US performance on what TV show?

⑥ Which US state has only one syllable?

⑦ How many times was Niki Lauda Formula 1 world champion?

⑧ What was Thomas Hardy's last novel?

⑨ In *Wayne's World*, what is Wayne's surname?

⑩ Who was Bruce Forsyth's second wife?

⑪ Which part of the Vatican is used for the election of a Pope?

⑫ What musical instrument did Pablo Casals play?

⑬ Which is the only UK town with an exclamation mark in its name?

⑭ Who won an Oscar for the screenplay of *Gosford Park*?

⑮ Cosima Von Bülow was married to which composer?

⑯ Who dubbed Audrey Hepburn's singing voice in *My Fair Lady*?

QUIZ 218

① Was Ronald Reagan left- or right-handed?

② What does ambisinistrous mean?

③ Who became the Scarecrow in *The Wizard of Oz*?

④ And who played the Scarecrow in the film?

⑤ What is *Where's Wally?* called in the USA?

⑥ Lake Taupo is on which New Zealand island?

⑦ In which year did ice skater Robin Cousins win an Olympic gold?

⑧ How is Hansen's disease more familiarly known?

⑨ Which two countries signed the 'Pact of Steel' in 1939?

⑩ What type of animal is a capuchin?

⑪ Which English prime minister was called the 'Great Commoner'?

⑫ Whose autobiography was *Memoirs of an Unfit Mother*?

⑬ Who was the first wicket-keeper to score 4000 runs in Tests?

⑭ Which woman did former 'Miss USA' Lynda Carter become?

⑮ Who is known as the 'fifth' Beatle?

⑯ Name the wife and frequent co-star of actor Yves Montand.

QUIZ 219

① Who was The Beatles' manager who committed suicide in 1967?

② What is a single upright monumental stone called?

③ Which English poet's first names were Alfred Edward?

④ What is a bass singer with an exceptionally low range called?

⑤ Who led an armed rebellion against Henry III in 1264?

⑥ Which celebrated cook was born Isabella Mary Mayson?

⑦ 'Have Yourself A Merry Little Christmas' comes from which film?

⑧ Which cricket ODI trophy do Australia and New Zealand play for?

⑨ What rare birds breed at Loch Garton in Scotland?

⑩ Who wrote the play *Chips With Everything*?

⑪ What is a 'growler'?

⑫ Name the author of *The Rise and Fall of the Third Reich*.

⑬ With which stage star was Prince Edward romantically involved?

⑭ Who did Zinedine Zidane headbutt in the 2006 World Cup final?

⑮ Which is the older London tunnel, Blackwall or Rotherhithe?

⑯ Which 1970s pop group had the name of a US bomber?

QUIZ 220

① Which English playwright was knighted in 2006?

② What do the explorer H M Stanley's initials stand for?

③ What is the name of Mackenzie Crook's character in *The Office*?

④ In which country is the Simpson Desert?

⑤ What type of hat did Buster Keaton often wear on screen?

⑥ At which club did the Eric Cantona 'kung-fu' incident occur?

⑦ Who is older, Tim Rice or Andrew Lloyd Webber?

⑧ What is the only dog mentioned in the Bible?

⑨ What is Schubert's Symphony No 8 informally called?

⑩ What did Francis Crick and James Watson unravel?

⑪ In police jargon, what is TWOC?

⑫ What is the full title of *The Pickwick Papers*?

⑬ What type of creature is an aye-aye?

⑭ And which island is its exclusive address?

⑮ What career did Bob Geldof have before show business?

⑯ In which English county is the Fylde Peninsula?

QUIZ 221

① Which word can be a young knight or part of a book?

② What institution did George Williams found in London in 1844?

③ Who was the first left-hander to win a major golf championship?

④ Spider, Traffic and Twingo are all models of which car?

⑤ Which animals were the subject of *Ring of Bright Water*?

⑥ In which galaxy will you find the Pistol Star?

⑦ To whom was Madonna married between 1985 and 1989?

⑧ What does the Bible say came first, chicken or egg?

⑨ Which veteran Hollywood actor is in the TV series *Mad Men*?

⑩ What is the feathered plume on a military headdress called?

⑪ Who were the last winners of the rugby Five Nations?

⑫ What was Frank Sinatra's favourite style of hat?

⑬ In which year did Prince Charles marry Lady Diana Spencer?

⑭ What does the Latin phrase *cave canem* mean?

⑮ Zeta comes where in the Greek alphabet?

⑯ What do the Americans call an eiderdown?

QUIZ 222

① How many times does Scarlett O'Hara marry in *Gone With the Wind*?

② Which French dance violently portrays a gangster with his woman?

③ Where in London is the famous Royal Court Theatre?

④ Tennis star Pam Shriver was married to which 'James Bond'?

⑤ What is the American term for grilling food?

⑥ Steinway and Bösendorfer are makes of what?

⑦ Who did Marie-Christine von Reibnitz become in 1978?

⑧ Does a skipjack skip, jump or swim?

⑨ What was an 'Iron Maiden'?

⑩ Which pioneer aviatrix was drowned parachuting into the Thames?

⑪ In what profession is a dolly grip employed?

⑫ Which two rugby teams compete for the Bowring Bowl?

⑬ Who launched Fox News in 1996?

⑭ In which state is the TV animated town of South Park?

⑮ Who wrote the song 'A Little Bit Me, A Little Bit You'?

⑯ Tchaikovsky's opera *The Queen of Spades* is based on whose story?

QUIZ 223

1. In which year did Cyprus gain its independence?

2. Who wrote 'The Battle Hymn of the Republic'?

3. In Greek mythology, who fell in love with the statue he carved?

4. Which driver posthumously won the F1 World Championship in 1970?

5. Who was captain of the German cruiser *Admiral Graf Spee*?

6. And who played him in the film *Battle of the River Plate*?

7. Who wrote *The Daring Young Man on the Flying Trapeze*?

8. What is a lift that conveys food from kitchen to dining room?

9. What headwear is made from the leaves of the toquilla straw plant?

10. Whose last words were: 'Get my swan costume ready.'?

11. How was Dickens' illustrator Hablot Browne better known?

12. What do the initials stand for in O J Simpson?

13. What was the Spice Girls' Christmas hit of 1998?

14. What is Yorkshire fog when it is not a mist?

15. Who embarrassingly resigned from the Royal Marines in 1987?

16. What surname goes with Edith, Osbert and Sacheverell?

QUIZ 224
GEOGRAPHY

① In which US mountain range is Lake Tahoe situated?

② What is an erg?

③ Jèrriais is the local language of where?

④ Monrovia is the capital of which West African country?

⑤ Which landlocked African nation's capital is Gabarone?

⑥ Where are the Troodos mountains?

⑦ Which country is to the north of Nigeria?

⑧ Which sea is located north of Norway and Russia?

⑨ What is the 'City of a Thousand Minarets'?

⑩ Where is the port of Pusan?

⑪ What is the official name of New York's Sixth Avenue?

⑫ Which desert contains the driest place on earth?

⑬ What country is also known as Lettland?

⑭ French Guiana's capital shares its name with which pepper?

⑮ What is a part of North America but belongs to Denmark?

⑯ Which part of Greece is autonomous?

QUIZ 225

① What was the sequel to Louisa May Alcott's *Little Women*?

② How many golf championships make up the Majors?

③ What is another name for a pith helmet?

④ Who plays Detective Nordberg in the *Naked Gun* films?

⑤ What UK licence was abolished in 1987?

⑥ Who escaped from Colditz and wrote a book about it?

⑦ How many Wimbledon championships did Suzanne Lenglen win?

⑧ What is a baby hare called?

⑨ Who was the founder of Singapore?

⑩ In the Bible, what building led to the confusion of languages?

⑪ What does *flagrante delicto* mean?

⑫ In which year was the Heysel Stadium disaster?

⑬ What is another name for the Arabian camel?

⑭ Logo is derived from the Greek word for what?

⑮ Who does Peter Lorre play in *The Maltese Falcon*?

⑯ What does Addis Ababa mean?

QUIZ 226

① Which ballooning duo crossed the Atlantic in July 1987?

② With which English seaside town is the artist J M W Turner particularly associated?

③ Is a porpoise a fish or a mammal?

④ In which English cathedral is the Mappa Mundi housed?

⑤ Who plays Perry to Harry Enfield's Kevin?

⑥ What does the French word *atelier* mean?

⑦ How were cricket pitches marked before whitewash?

⑧ Who was the Boomtown Rats' lead vocalist?

⑨ In which year was VAT first introduced in the UK?

⑩ Which country was once known as New Spain?

⑪ Which film actor's real name is Krishna Bhanji?

⑫ The name of which US state means 'Feast of Flowers'?

⑬ Hugh Lofting created which famous children's character?

⑭ Which European language is spoken in Chad?

⑮ What type of garment is a 'poor boy'?

⑯ Which animal has the longest tail?

QUIZ 227

① What does *mens sana in corpore sano* mean?

② To what family of animals does the yak belong?

③ What is the name of the US national cemetery in Washington?

④ What was the Glastonbury Festival originally called?

⑤ To which planet do the moons Titan, Rhea and Lapetus belong?

⑥ Which British prime minister introduced income tax in 1799?

⑦ What is a burro?

⑧ Which oil rig exploded in the Gulf of Mexico in 2010?

⑨ Which novel did Charles Dickens fail to finish?

⑩ What was the name of Lord Louis Mountbatten's wife?

⑪ What ancient relics are disputed by Greece and the UK?

⑫ Which empire was Cuzco the capital of?

⑬ Which financier was christened 'Goldenballs' by *Private Eye*?

⑭ Camogie is the women's version of which sport?

⑮ What colour is the middle stripe of the Austrian flag?

⑯ Who musically hit the road with his 'Funky Moped' in 1975?

QUIZ 228

① What word is something you look at or means looking for something?

② Which came first, *Daily Express* or *Daily Mail*?

③ Yossarian is the anti-hero of which iconic 20th-century novel?

④ Which prince's last words were: 'Good little woman.'?

⑤ Spell the name of the river celebrated by Mark Twain.

⑥ Boris Johnson is the ex-editor of which national magazine?

⑦ In which sport might you perform a fliffis?

⑧ What did Dennis Tito become in 2001?

⑨ Orson Welles was the 'voice' of which TV lager commercials?

⑩ Which 60s hit was inspired by explorer Thor Heyerdahl's raft?

⑪ Which film actress began life as Margaret Hyra?

⑫ In which US state are the Black Hills?

⑬ The original members of Genesis went to which public school?

⑭ Who is the resident scientist on *The Muppet Show*?

⑮ How many innings per game are there in baseball?

⑯ The name of the drink Sangria literally means what?

QUIZ 229

① Was Ellis Peters, creator of Cadfael, male or female?

② What does 'brut' on a bottle of wine signify?

③ In which year, in Roman numerals, did Elvis Presley die?

④ What TV duo were chefs Antonio Carluccio and Gennaro Contaldo?

⑤ Which word can precede beer, bread and nut?

⑥ What does a sawyer do?

⑦ Which film star was nicknamed the 'professional virgin'?

⑧ What is the capital of Liechtenstein?

⑨ What publication did John Bird and Gordon Roddick found in 1991?

⑩ Which iconic US rock festival took place in 1969?

⑪ What is rugby's Calcutta Cup made from?

⑫ Who directed the film *Thelma and Louise*?

⑬ Which country's launch rockets are called 'Long March'?

⑭ What is a female ferret called?

⑮ What are the Everly Brothers' first names?

⑯ What type of creature is a racer?

QUIZ 230

1. Which international airline went bust in 1991?

2. What is French wine of the highest grade called?

3. Who wrote *As I Walked Out One Midsummer Morning*?

4. What is a *bouzouki*?

5. Muscovy was a former region of which modern nation?

6. What was the Elizabethan word for 'please'?

7. Where was Prince Charles invested as Prince of Wales?

8. Which US president's head is on a one dollar bill?

9. What was the world's first jet airliner?

10. What did Thames Ironworks FC change its name to in 1900?

11. Which comedy duo had their only hit with 'The Stonk' in 1991?

12. In which 1898 war did the Rough Riders play a prominent part?

13. What is the Scottish word for a strait or channel of water?

14. In dentistry, what are caries?

15. Which city is home to the Concertgebouw Orchestra?

16. What is the high-jump event in show jumping called?

QUIZ 231
SPORT

① Which British Indianapolis 500 winner was killed in 2011?

② Which cricketer played 153 successive Tests for Australia?

③ Who scored France's try in the 2011 Rugby World Cup final?

④ Which skier won three gold medals at the 1968 Winter Olympics?

⑤ Where was the game of squash invented?

⑥ Which British driver won the F1 World Championship in 1976?

⑦ Who did Roger Federer beat in his first Wimbledon final?

⑧ Who was the Football Writers' 2010 Player of the Year?

⑨ Where is the Test cricket ground of McLean Park?

⑩ Add the sporting surname: Adam and Ben . . .

⑪ Which sport features in the 1979 film *Breaking Away*?

⑫ Which world champion heavyweight's real name was Arnold Cream?

⑬ Who was Manchester United's manager before Alex Ferguson?

⑭ Which former England footballer was knighted in 1998?

⑮ Who in 1900 became the first Olympic rugby champions?

⑯ Who was *Wisden's* first female Cricketer of the Year?

QUIZ 232

① Who was the 'Naked Civil Servant'?

② Which British DJ died in 2006?

③ Which French phrase in common usage means 'in relation to'?

④ What nationality is the mobile phone company Nokia?

⑤ What is a male donkey called?

⑥ To which family of flowers does the asphodel belong?

⑦ Who was Margaret Thatcher's last Chancellor of the Exchequer?

⑧ What in literary terms is a saw?

⑨ Ian Botham made his Test debut against which country?

⑩ What can be a bird of prey or a hunting dog?

⑪ Which Russian spy was irradiated in London in 2006?

⑫ What is Florida's state capital?

⑬ Who attended the 2001 Oscars dressed like a swan?

⑭ What was scientist Sir Joseph Banks' specialist subject?

⑮ Who was the first UK female singer to win a BRIT award?

⑯ How long did it take aviator Louis Blériot to cross the English Channel in 1909?

QUIZ 233

① Which is the UK's longest motorway?

② Whose head is on the reverse side of a £10 note?

③ Rheims is the centre of which French wine region?

④ Which mineral are bananas rich in?

⑤ What is a small rowing boat for one person called?

⑥ How often do neap tides occur?

⑦ What is the lightest weight category in professional boxing?

⑧ What is a white English-speaking person called in South America?

⑨ North Dakota's capital is the name of which German statesman?

⑩ What do you fear if you are parthenophobic?

⑪ On which instrument would you play a paradiddle-diddle?

⑫ In what year was the Chernobyl nuclear disaster?

⑬ The Cylons were evil robots in which TV series?

⑭ Which breed of dog has webbed feet?

⑮ Lord Nuffield was the UK's first mass producer of what?

⑯ Who was lead vocalist in Genesis before Phil Collins?

QUIZ 234

① The inhabitants of Martinique are citizens of which country?

② In which county is the National Memorial Arboretum?

③ From what is rayon produced?

④ What game means 'I play' in Latin?

⑤ In which US city is the Liberty Bell?

⑥ What is the collar badge of the Irish Guards?

⑦ 'Tubular Bells' was the theme of which 1973 movie?

⑧ What does ZIP, as in zip codes, stand for?

⑨ In which US city was the first Playboy Club opened?

⑩ How is Te Whanganui-a-Tara in New Zealand better known?

⑪ What is the text of an opera called?

⑫ *L'heure bleue* is French for what?

⑬ In the game of poker, what is a horse?

⑭ What type of state is Liechtenstein?

⑮ In which UK city is St Enoch Square?

⑯ What does a limnologist study?

QUIZ 235

① Which British Formula One motor-racing driver died in 1993?

② Which statesman features on a US $100 bill?

③ Who was the first bowler to take a Test hat-trick?

④ *The Audacity of Hope* is whose political doctrine?

⑤ Who sang 'Happy Birthday' to Prince Charles on his 50th?

⑥ What were sailors from India or southeast Asia called?

⑦ Who captained Europe in the 2006 Ryder Cup?

⑧ What wind speed makes a storm a hurricane?

⑨ What lake is between the north and south parts of the Suez Canal?

⑩ Which great female opera singer was born in Sydney in 1926?

⑪ Who is Boris Johnson's journalist sister?

⑫ What type of bird is a gentoo?

⑬ Who said: 'Go West, young man . . .'?

⑭ What does the name Swindon mean?

⑮ What poem begins: 'Wee, sleekit, cow'rin, tim'rous beastie . .'?

⑯ Who dressed the part when singing 'Tears of a Clown'?

QUIZ 236

① Which UK coin ceased to be legal tender in 1970?

② Who resigned as Director General of the BBC in 2004?

③ In the American West, what is a wild or half-tamed horse called?

④ Whose family cookie recipe in *Friends* proved to be a fake?

⑤ What is a sphygmomanometer used to monitor?

⑥ What is a preliminary report of a government proposal called?

⑦ Who was Peter Mandelson's politician grandfather?

⑧ What represents the final goal of Buddhism?

⑨ Which super-tanker ran aground off the Brittany coast in 1978?

⑩ What is a bight?

⑪ Which country's national flag features a cedar tree?

⑫ What is the field of play in American football called?

⑬ At what time of day is the First Post sounded in the army?

⑭ Who played private eye Mike Hammer on TV in the 1980s?

⑮ What is the USA's highest civilian award?

⑯ Who threw iced water over John Prescott at the 1998 BRITS?

QUIZ 237

① Which North Sea oil rig disastrously caught fire in 1988?

② Who was transferred from the FA to the Royal Mail in 2003?

③ What sport is toxophily?

④ Which architect designed Brighton's Regency Royal Pavilion?

⑤ How many BRITS did Dusty Springfield win?

⑥ What became the Queen Mother's new address in 1953?

⑦ In Greek mythology, who was the father of Icarus?

⑧ What does a butterfly use for feeding?

⑨ Six-line, Street and Corner are all what?

⑩ Who was the jockey knighted in 1953?

⑪ How many statues are on the Charles Bridge in Prague?

⑫ What in mathematics is a googol?

⑬ Who had a hit in 2002 with 'C'Mon, C'Mon'?

⑭ What Central American country's name means 'rich coast'?

⑮ Who played Soames in the original TV series of *The Forsyte Saga*?

⑯ Which country staged its first Formula One race in 2005?

QUIZ 238

① Who is on the reverse side of a £20 note?

② What colour plume is on the Coldstream Guards' bearskins?

③ What is a 'Dear Abby' in the USA?

④ Name the nuclear sub that ran aground in a Scottish loch in 2010.

⑤ Who was the high-profile wife of Mikhail Gorbachev?

⑥ In a deck of cards which king doesn't have a moustache?

⑦ Which common insect has taste buds on its feet?

⑧ How many feet in a fathom?

⑨ Add the sporting surname: Colin and Christopher . . .

⑩ In which TV series does the 13th Duke of Wybourne appear?

⑪ Which is Europe's smallest state?

⑫ Who wrote the music for the film *The Magnificent Seven*?

⑬ Are own goals allowed in hockey?

⑭ Which country is south-east of Honduras?

⑮ What metal is made from bauxite?

⑯ Which South African Test cricketer was banned from the sport for six months in 2000?

QUIZ 239
CINEMA & TV

① What was Madonna's first film?

② Which playwright plays a major role in the film *Get Carter*?

③ What is TV Egghead CJ's surname?

④ Which comic had a 1990s TV show called *The Man from Auntie*?

⑤ Which film director shares the name of a famous explorer?

⑥ Who played Captain Brown in *Cranford*?

⑦ In the film *The Lion King* whose voice is that of Scar?

⑧ Name the other half: Jemaine Clement and . . .

⑨ Who is writer Sharman Macdonald's more famous actress daughter?

⑩ Which *Mad Men* character goes from secretary to copywriter?

⑪ Which former US teenage star became a cocktail waitress?

⑫ Who on screen plays the girl with the dragon tattoo?

⑬ And what is the name of her character?

⑭ Who was Dr Kildare's mentor?

⑮ Three consecutive generations of which family have won Oscars?

⑯ Which actor's first name means in Hawaiian 'Cool breeze over the mountain'?

QUIZ 240

① What sort of a cape did Sherlock Holmes wear?

② Flattop, Butch and Buzz are all types of what?

③ Which president's wife was executed with her husband in 1989?

④ What family of plant is bamboo?

⑤ On a motorbike what is the 'softail'?

⑥ What common pub sign celebrates a king's narrow escape?

⑦ What shade of green is traditional tweed?

⑧ Name the first England soccer player sent off in an international.

⑨ Who mistakes Alice (in Wonderland) for his housemaid Mary Ann?

⑩ What is the longest enclosed glen in Scotland?

⑪ Rock salmon is another name for what?

⑫ What are the Major Arcana?

⑬ Where in Italy is Syracuse?

⑭ Where in the USA is Syracuse?

⑮ Which Falklands War recipient of the VC was known as 'H'?

⑯ Who died one month before '(Sittin' On) The Dock Of The Bay' was released?

QUIZ 241

① Who was appointed Master of the Queen's Music in 2004?

② Which UK coin ceased to be legal tender in 1960?

③ Piquet, Belote and Skat are all types of what?

④ Dogri is a language in which two Asian countries?

⑤ What is the fictional character Harry Angstrom's nickname?

⑥ Yosemite, as in the US national park, means what?

⑦ What part of the oak tree is used for tanning leather?

⑧ A Centurian or Custodian helmet is worn by whom?

⑨ *Seven Brides for Seven Brothers* was based on which Roman legend?

⑩ In lacrosse, which team has more members: men's or women's?

⑪ How many points does the star on the Moroccan flag have?

⑫ What word can be a spirit or reflect something strange?

⑬ Which is Europe's highest capital city?

⑭ Who had a hit with 'It's Raining Men'?

⑮ Which US serial killer gave himself an astrological nickname?

⑯ Cherbourg is at the head of which French peninsula?

QUIZ 242

① Whose head appears on a US $10 bill?

② Which film company did George Harrison co-found?

③ What were the lower classes of the French Revolution called?

④ And what does the term literally mean?

⑤ Who was presented with an Oscar on stage in London in 2011?

⑥ What was the name of the 'Oklahoma Bomber'?

⑦ Where do poinsettias originate?

⑧ Which UK historian was jailed in 2006 for denying the Holocaust?

⑨ Who composed the *Kreutzer Sonata*?

⑩ Who wrote the novella the *Kreutzer Sonata*?

⑪ Who had a hit with the title song from the film *The Crying Game*?

⑫ Which English monarch was born at Fotheringhay Castle?

⑬ Who scored the first golden goal in football World Cup history?

⑭ And when and against whom did he score it?

⑮ How is Victoria Hesketh better known?

⑯ Which river forms a border between China and North Korea?

QUIZ 243

1. Which British regiment's nickname is the 'Angle-irons'?

2. Flexible, Treeless and Double Seat are all types of what?

3. Add the showbiz surname: Jonathan and Paul . . .

4. What is the head of the Eastern Orthodox Church called?

5. Who spilled the beans about Monica Lewinsky and Bill Clinton?

6. What is a glengarry?

7. Polenta flour comes from the seed of which tree?

8. In what part of the UK is a dog licence still required?

9. What was the name of Kate Winslet's character in *Titanic*?

10. Which is nearer to London: Amsterdam or Paris?

11. In bingo, what number is 'Jump and jive'?

12. Where in Spain is there a major annual film festival?

13. What nationality was composer Malcolm Williamson?

14. Which city's airport was previously called 'Kingsford-Smith'?

15. On which animal other than a horse is polo played?

16. Who was the first woman to sail solo non-stop around the world in both directions?

QUIZ 244

① Who invented playing cards?

② Which holy city was previously called Bakkah?

③ What is the former Oxford Polytechnic called?

④ Who represents the Crown in each county of the UK?

⑤ The pohutukawa tree is native to which country?

⑥ What was Queen Victoria's first name?

⑦ Who said: 'Don't count the days, make the days count.'?

⑧ What word can precede head, house and rod?

⑨ In which 19th-century novel does Svengali first appear?

⑩ And who wrote the novel?

⑪ Which English operetta is sub-titled 'The King of Barataria'?

⑫ How old was Stanley Matthews when he played his last game?

⑬ Which part of a flower protects its bud?

⑭ What was the movie sequel to *Love Story*?

⑮ Who recorded 'Clint Eastwood' in 2001?

⑯ What does the name Ely mean?

QUIZ 245

① What animal walked behind the coffin at Edward VII's funeral?

② Who co-hosted the Oscars in 2011?

③ Which 'royal' won a sailing gold medal at the Rome Olympics?

④ What moss is found in peat bogs?

⑤ Which pair rowed across the Atlantic in 1966?

⑥ Who was Anne Boleyn's infamous sister?

⑦ Who was Cher's second husband?

⑧ Manchego is a cheese from which country?

⑨ How old was Michael Chang when he won the French tennis Open?

⑩ What was the first club to concede 100 Premiership goals?

⑪ The 24-hour Le Mans race is held in which month of the year?

⑫ After which US athlete was Lewis Hamilton named?

⑬ Tobermory is on which Scottish island?

⑭ Which is nearer to London: Budapest or Rome?

⑮ Who are EWF?

⑯ What is the world's biggest-selling single malt whisky?

QUIZ 246
SCIENCE & NATURE

① Slipper, Spiny and Squat are all varieties of what?

② Who was appointed Astronomer Royal in 1995?

③ Snails belong to which group of animals?

④ In which human body organ is the 'Loop of Henle'?

⑤ How is the Lent lily better known?

⑥ What does the Latin word *morbus* mean?

⑦ Which fish spends much of its time out of water?

⑧ What is a male wolf called?

⑨ In which country is the Siding Spring Observatory?

⑩ Do flying fish actually fly?

⑪ What is the world's largest frog?

⑫ Troy weights are used for measuring what?

⑬ Name the inventor of the rotary car engine.

⑭ What flower shares its name with a musical instrument?

⑮ Who wrote *Principia Mathematica*?

⑯ What do you aggravate when you hit your 'funny bone'?

QUIZ 247

① Espada, Jarama and Diablo are all models of which car?

② Which fellow writer was married to Jean-Paul Sartre?

③ What is Japanese food dipped in batter and deep-fried?

④ If two people are osculating, what are they doing?

⑤ Which was the first nation to ratify the UN Charter in 1945?

⑥ What 18th-century hairstyle did Jeanne Antoinette Poisson create?

⑦ Which cat had an obituary in *Wisden Cricketers' Almanack*?

⑧ What is the largest of London's subterranean rivers?

⑨ The memorial to Princess Diana in Hyde Park is a what?

⑩ Who is the 'Queen of Hip-Hop Soul'?

⑪ What does MOBO stand for?

⑫ What was the KGB's notorious headquarters in Moscow?

⑬ What is North Korea's full name?

⑭ And what is its capital city?

⑮ Which English king popularized the homburg hat?

⑯ Who was the leading exponent of the art of mime?

QUIZ 248

① In which country was Mel Gibson born?

② What is the Wimbledon Ladies' Singles trophy?

③ Who does Anthony Head play in *Buffy the Vampire Slayer*?

④ What are the four principal blood groups?

⑤ In which palace was Queen Victoria born?

⑥ If you are ponophobic what are you afraid of?

⑦ Who is the author of the Tilly Trotter books?

⑧ Who was the last English king to lead his army into battle?

⑨ How many colours are there on the Seychelles flag?

⑩ Who was the first non-American to win the US Masters?

⑪ Which is Scotland's longest river?

⑫ What nationality is the novelist Nadine Gordimer?

⑬ What is Switzerland divided into?

⑭ In boxing, what is a 'palooka'?

⑮ Who painted *The Starry Night*?

⑯ What London landmark was destroyed by fire sixteen days after it opened in 1873?

QUIZ 249

1. In which country was the artist Hans Holbein the Younger born?

2. What did the 1819 massacre in Manchester become known as?

3. Which 17th-century writer and 20th-century artist share the same name?

4. What is the name of Winston Churchill's former home in Kent?

5. What insect produces 'cuckoo spit'?

6. Who was known as the 'Brylcreem Boy'?

7. What revolutionary camera did Edwin Land invent?

8. In *M*A*S*H* what is Hawkeye's full name?

9. What does the Latin phrase *tabula rasa* mean?

10. Yellowknife is the capital of which region of Canada?

11. What is the largest prehistoric monument in England?

12. When did the Davis Cup competition begin: 1900, 1910, 1920?

13. Add the showbiz surname: Eric and Julia . . .

14. Who in the play *Hamlet* says: 'Brevity is the soul of wit'?

15. In which year did baseball become an Olympic sport?

16. Which US state is called the 'Nutmeg State'?

QUIZ 250

① On what part of the human body is the skin thinnest?

② What was the cruise ship in the TV series *The Love Boat*?

③ In which year did the Queen Mother reach her century?

④ Who wrote the poem 'Comin' thro' the Rye'?

⑤ What is a female bear called?

⑥ Whose catchphrase was 'Rock on, Tommy'?

⑦ Which US state is further north, Connecticut or Massachusetts?

⑧ Who conducted the first royal TV interview in 1961?

⑨ Who is the first Muslim ever to play for the All Blacks?

⑩ What breed of dog is a Clumber?

⑪ In which London bank did the poet T S Eliot work?

⑫ Who became Britain's youngest ever Olympian in 1960?

⑬ In which English national park is Yes Tor?

⑭ Where was Nicole Kidman born?

⑮ Who composed the march *Crown Imperial*?

⑯ In which year did Nick Faldo win The Open and The US Masters?

QUIZ 251

① Who became prime minister first, Gladstone or Disraeli?

② Which English sculptor lived at Much Hadham?

③ How many were in the 60s group The Mamas & the Papas?

④ What is the collective name for tigers?

⑤ Who became New York's first billionaire mayor in 2001?

⑥ What musical instruction means 'fast'?

⑦ Which UK actress played Ross' wife in *Friends*?

⑧ Which golfer won her first Women's British Open in 1995?

⑨ What is the highest mountain in Portugal?

⑩ Who was Viscount Linley's father?

⑪ Which ex-Nazi became Austria's president in 1986?

⑫ Leopold Bloom is the central character in which novel?

⑬ What is the name of the world's largest gulf?

⑭ Which 1980s TV series starred Emma Thompson and Robbie Coltrane?

⑮ What type of fruit is a bullace?

⑯ Martin Adams and Phil Taylor were both 2010 world champions in which sport?

QUIZ 252

① Who was the Swedish prime minister assassinated in 1986?

② Which Lord Chancellor died in 1535 defending his principles?

③ On which island did the poet Robert Graves live?

④ Which four US presidents can be seen at Mount Rushmore?

⑤ What is 'Count' Basie's first name?

⑥ Which poet wrote the *Barrack-Room Ballads*?

⑦ What is the world's smallest species of bear?

⑧ How old was Bjorn Borg when he retired from mainstream tennis?

⑨ What was the name of the first orbital space station?

⑩ Who succeeded King Hussein of Jordan in 1999?

⑪ Which British writer won the Nobel Prize in Literature in 1932?

⑫ Which darts champion is nicknamed the 'Crafty Cockney'?

⑬ What is the official language of Liechtenstein?

⑭ The film *Somebody Up There Likes Me* is about which boxer?

⑮ London's Green Park tube station was formerly called what?

⑯ The island of Ithaca is in which sea?

QUIZ 253

① Who was the first UK footballer to notch 1,000 top-level games?

② What is measured in metres per second?

③ Who shared the 1978 Nobel Peace Prize?

④ What is a Polynesian garland of flowers or shells called?

⑤ Elijah Blue Allman is the son of which US singer/actress?

⑥ What was the last movie watched by gangster John Dillinger?

⑦ Why did several countries boycott the 1956 Olympics?

⑧ Which desert contains elephants, lions and giraffes?

⑨ In which city was Tony Blair born?

⑩ Who played the title role in the film *Annie*?

⑪ Which US erotic dancer took Paris by storm in the 1920s?

⑫ What was the title of the BBC's first early morning TV show?

⑬ And who were its first presenters?

⑭ How many Confederate States of America were there?

⑮ What in show business is an ecdysiast?

⑯ In the nursery rhyme, what did the crooked man find?

QUIZ 254
MUSIC

① What group headlined the opening of the O2 arena in 2005?

② For whom did Paul McCartney write 'Hey Jude'?

③ What was Amy Winehouse's first posthumous album?

④ Which film launched the song 'White Christmas'?

⑤ Which popular Cuban song became a 60s hit for The Sandpipers?

⑥ Who composed *Peter and the Wolf*?

⑦ How many keys are there on a standard piano?

⑧ What provided the words for Carla Bruni's 2007 album *No Promises*?

⑨ Who was the first black soloist to sing at the New York Met?

⑩ How many variations make up Elgar's enigmatic classic?

⑪ Which alternative rock group does Dave Grohl front?

⑫ What was Cliff Richard's Christmas song for 2003?

⑬ Who supported 'Cool Britannia' by playing a Union Flag guitar?

⑭ Which Russian mystic did Bony M sing about in 1978?

⑮ Which veteran singer won his first BRIT in 2000?

⑯ Who was sacked by The Precision Tool Company in 1951 for being under age?

QUIZ 255

① What was the name of the 1970s British terrorist group?

② How old was Cary Grant when he married for the fifth time?

③ Which motor-cycling world champion died in a car crash in 1981?

④ Meteorologically speaking, what are 'mare's tails'?

⑤ What was the painter Canaletto's real surname?

⑥ Who did Ronnie Corbett play in the TV sitcom *Sorry!*?

⑦ Who in 1979 became Britain's first million-pound footballer?

⑧ Complete the title of the H G Wells novel, *Love and* . . .

⑨ Who was stripped of his gold medal at the Seoul Olympics?

⑩ Harold Macmillan married into which ducal family?

⑪ Which cricketer is nicknamed the 'Rawalpindi Express'?

⑫ What is the boundary that divides the two parts of Cyprus?

⑬ Which sporting first did Charlotte Brew achieve in 1977?

⑭ Who wrote the epic poem 'John Brown's Body'?

⑮ What direction indicates two or more actors leaving the stage?

⑯ UK scientist Godfrey Hounsfield won the 1979 Nobel Prize in Medicine for inventing what?

QUIZ 256

① On which circuit was racing driver Jim Clark killed in 1968?

② Who did Harold Wilson succeed as leader of the Labour Party?

③ Which great British actor died in 1833?

④ Which male star became the fragrant face of Givenchy in 2008?

⑤ Which two books in the Bible have a woman's name in the title?

⑥ What was Fred Astaire's main preoccupation in retirement?

⑦ What kind of rock are limestone and sandstone?

⑧ How was double agent Eddie Chapman known in intelligence circles?

⑨ Which UK home secretary resigned in 1972 over the Poulson Affair?

⑩ Michael Manley was prime minister of which Caribbean island?

⑪ Has croquet ever been an Olympic sport?

⑫ What is the provincial capital of Saskatchewan in Canada?

⑬ How many laps are there in a speedway heat?

⑭ What were the better-off Russian peasants called?

⑮ How old was Dino Zoff when he won a medal in the 1982 World Cup?

⑯ What is another name for kettle drums?

QUIZ 257

① Which couple were known as 'Bennifer'?

② In which country was Carling beer first brewed?

③ If you become endentulous what will you have lost?

④ What is gypsum also known as?

⑤ Was the author H P Lovecraft, male or female?

⑥ What is New York City's principal seat of learning?

⑦ How was Baroness Olivier better known on stage?

⑧ In which airline did Howard Hughes have a controlling interest?

⑨ 'Sprazzy' and 'Simon' were slang terms for which former UK coin?

⑩ Who was the first golfer to win $1m in prize money?

⑪ What is the capital of Luxembourg?

⑫ Which 'royal' was a panellist in *Question of Sport* in 1987?

⑬ Whose debut album was *Ten Good Reasons*?

⑭ Which pair of Swiss scientists and inventors were twins?

⑮ In which country was the magician Harry Houdini born?

⑯ Which US Beat Generation novelist died in 1969?

QUIZ 258

① Which Scottish city lies between the Dee and the Don?

② Who was Andre Agassi's first wife?

③ In which German city was Anne Frank born?

④ What nationality was Omar Khayyám?

⑤ Which galaxy is nearest to our own?

⑥ What did Giorgio Armani study before fashion?

⑦ Who led the British Lions to victory in New Zealand in 1971?

⑧ What is the second largest city in France?

⑨ Inspector Claud Eustace Teal is a fictional adversary of whom?

⑩ What in the Bible are sometimes called 'The Decalogue'?

⑪ *Tko zeli biti milijunas?* is what TV game show in Croatia?

⑫ Bennetts Irongate in Derby is the UK's oldest what?

⑬ What was the first league club managed by Martin O'Neill?

⑭ Who in 2005 registered the UK's 1000th No 1 Single?

⑮ Which is the London market featured in TV's *Market Kitchen*?

⑯ When it is noon at GMT, what time is it in Rio de Janeiro?

QUIZ 259

① Who was the first UK winner of *Who Wants To Be A Millionaire*?

② Old gold coins of Spain and Spanish America were called what?

③ Who led England to victory in the 2009 women's cricket World Cup?

④ Name the space telescope launched in 1990.

⑤ What is Hawkeye's real name in *The Last of the Mohicans*?

⑥ And who wrote the novel?

⑦ Which pop duo won *nul points* in the 2003 Eurovision Song Contest?

⑧ What is the national bird of the USA?

⑨ Ushanka, Montera and Keffiyeh are all types of what?

⑩ On what day of the week was President Kennedy killed?

⑪ Who was sportingly known as 'Pistol Pete'?

⑫ Which is the largest city in the Basque Country?

⑬ Who composed the symphony known as 'The Age of Anxiety'?

⑭ What was the political union between Germany and Austria called?

⑮ In which region of Italy is Naples?

⑯ Which UK comedian began his act with 'Hello my darlings'?

QUIZ 260

① What is the female equivalent of the USA's 'Uncle Sam'?

② 'Your flexible friend' was the slogan for which credit card?

③ What is Elton John's middle name?

④ Which hat was also known as a 'Bombin' or 'Billycock'?

⑤ What do the initials stand for in CAT scan?

⑥ What is the international dialling code for Ireland?

⑦ Name the squire in Robert Louis Stevenson's *Treasure Island*.

⑧ Which Formula One team shared the name of a sacred flower?

⑨ Mirandése is a regional language in which European country?

⑩ What was the most popular guide for 19th-century travellers?

⑪ Who composed the *Children's Corner* piano suite?

⑫ What is the only national capital beginning with Z?

⑬ Who played Julia Flyte in the 2008 film *Brideshead Revisited*?

⑭ How many goons were there in the original *Goon Show*?

⑮ What state is to the west of North Dakota?

⑯ The flowers of the ylang-ylang tree are used to make what?

QUIZ 261
HISTORY

① In what century were the Wars of the Roses fought?

② Which civilization built Machu Picchu?

③ Who burned Washington to the ground in 1814?

④ Which 20th-century British prime minister was born in Canada?

⑤ 'Red baiter' Joseph McCarthy was US senator for which state?

⑥ Where was David Lloyd George born?

⑦ Who was the American U2 pilot captured by the Russians in 1960?

⑧ Which title did Tony Benn disclaim in 1963?

⑨ Who did the French defeat at the Battle of Marengo in 1800?

⑩ Which US president survived two assassination attempts in 1975?

⑪ In which English county did the Battle of Bosworth take place?

⑫ What was the 1968 revolution in Czechoslovakia called?

⑬ Of which country was King Zog the ruler?

⑭ Who was the last British monarch to be born outside Britain?

⑮ In which year was the *Kristallnacht* pogrom in Germany?

⑯ How is Rodrigo Diaz de Vivar better known?

QUIZ 262

① What is the national symbol of Australia?

② In which card game is there a 'dead man's hand'?

③ Who was Rod Stewart divorced from in 2006?

④ What is 'Made in Scotland from girders'?

⑤ Who was the first British actor to play Maigret on television?

⑥ What does the musical instruction *glocoso* mean?

⑦ Who wrote *The Fist of God*?

⑧ In which sport is the Camanachd Cup contested?

⑨ What, sartorially speaking, does the Indian word *pagri* mean?

⑩ What is the term for a small rounded hill?

⑪ Which is further from London: Berlin or Copenhagen?

⑫ What are you having if you suffer a myocardial infarction?

⑬ Joe Cocker's 'Delta Lady' is dedicated to which singer?

⑭ In which seaside town was comedian Alan Carr born?

⑮ Name the Japanese writer who committed ritual suicide in 1970.

⑯ Under which name did Billie Jean King first play?

QUIZ 263

① What is the state capital of New York?

② Who was the first England football captain to be sent off?

③ And against which side was it?

④ Who followed William Wordsworth as Poet Laureate?

⑤ What is the 'It' in a Gin and It cocktail?

⑥ Which 'royal' is unflatteringly known as 'Princess Pushy'?

⑦ What fruit is naturally radioactive, though only slightly?

⑧ The Greater Adjutant is a member of which bird family?

⑨ How many countries border Germany?

⑩ Who plays Lord Percy Percy in *Blackadder*?

⑪ What is pneumonia?

⑫ What is the venue for the Australian Tennis Open?

⑬ When did McDonald's open its first fast-food outlet in London?

⑭ What material is used to make a sumo wrestling ring?

⑮ Which Fleet Street church was the spiritual home of journalists?

⑯ What was the name of Leo Tolstoy's long-suffering wife?

QUIZ 264

① Who said: 'When I want to read a book I write one'?

② What is the name of Tony and Cherie Blair's daughter?

③ What was the last football club that Roy Keane played for?

④ Who wears a biretta?

⑤ What was Admiral Nelson's great victory at sea in 1798?

⑥ Which city has more miles of canals, Birmingham or Venice?

⑦ Where in 1995 was the 'Million Man March' staged?

⑧ Which two countries does the Mont Cenis tunnel link?

⑨ 'Wotalotlgot' was the advertising slogan for which product?

⑩ Which British field marshal drowned at sea in 1916?

⑪ Who played the Artful Dodger in the film musical *Oliver!*?

⑫ The collapse of which bank precipitated the 2008 global crisis?

⑬ Who was awarded the 2010 Nobel Prize in Literature?

⑭ What was The Oval before it became a cricket ground in 1845?

⑮ Tussock, Burnet and Goat are all types of what?

⑯ What was the first Premier League club to go into administration?

QUIZ 265

① What TV series was set on Craggy Island?

② In the Bible, who is Abraham's wife?

③ Name the racist, homophobic character in *Little Britain*.

④ What is the Fourth Estate?

⑤ Which First Lady popularized the pillbox hat?

⑥ Who is the national personification of England?

⑦ What word describes changing into another form?

⑧ 'Strawberry' is a variety of what vegetable?

⑨ Which nation's military regiments wear a Canbeen?

⑩ With whom does Hamlet fight a duel?

⑪ Which rider in the Tour de France earns the *Lanterne Rouge*?

⑫ Who was the last Empress of India?

⑬ Which cricketing nation stages the Pura Cup competition?

⑭ Where in the human body is the *medulla oblongata*?

⑮ Which league club was previously called Singers FC?

⑯ Under which treaty did Britain recognize American independence?

QUIZ 266

1. In which country was the Boxer rebellion?

2. Ackee is the national fruit of which Caribbean island?

3. To where did General Douglas MacArthur vow to return?

4. Who was the first English Christian martyr?

5. What is the flower of a willow tree?

6. What did Harland Sanders found in 1952?

7. Which Australian became Somerset's cricket captain in 2001?

8. Who plays Larry David's wife in *Curb Your Enthusiasm*?

9. What aeronautical activity did Pussy Galore run?

10. Who wrote *The Compleat Angler*?

11. What is inscribed on the Victoria Cross?

12. Who was the first female presenter of *Blue Peter*?

13. What American currency took the form of shells and beads?

14. Who does Cpl Jones marry in *Dad's Army*?

15. The Eiffel Tower is adjacent to which park?

16. Who won the 2009 Rugby World Cup Sevens?

QUIZ 267

① Where was there a fatal crash on the London Underground in 1975?

② Who did Virginia Wade beat in the 1977 Wimbledon Ladies Final?

③ Which hostage was freed first, Brian Keenan or John McCarthy?

④ What does the Latin phrase *inter alia* mean?

⑤ Which 'royal' guested on *The Archers* in June 1984?

⑥ Who composed the opening theme music for *Coronation Street*?

⑦ Which female athlete won the first two London Marathons?

⑧ In cockney rhyming slang, what is Marie Corelli?

⑨ And who was Marie Corelli?

⑩ Which famous anthropologist wrote *Male and Female*?

⑪ Who made a topless appearance at Twickenham in 1982?

⑫ Where is the Welsh Grand National run?

⑬ In what country is the spa town of Spa?

⑭ Which president was the first occupant of the White House?

⑮ What is David Shilling best known for designing?

⑯ Interpol's headquarters is in which French city?

QUIZ 268

1) Who wrote the poem 'Ash Wednesday'?

2) Who was Egypt's first president?

3) What is a mendicant?

4) What town is at the foot of Ben Nevis?

5) What car company did Colin Chapman form in 1952?

6) What is the capital of Tahiti?

7) Who was the first UK driver to win the F1 World Championship?

8) What on the beat is a PCSO?

9) Which is further north, Carlisle or Newcastle?

10) In which US state is Yale University?

11) In 'Allo 'Allo what is René's surname?

12) What in Roman times was a publican?

13) When was Nelson's Column erected: 1823, 1833 or 1843?

14) What is the currency of Costa Rica?

15) In an open book which page is 'recto', left or right?

16) What is the tail of a whale?

QUIZ 269
GEOGRAPHY

1. What is the currency of Panama?

2. In which US state is Mount Rushmore?

3. Mt Kosciuszko is which country's highest mountain?

4. The zonda is a hot northerly wind in which S. American country?

5. In which English county are the Brimham Rocks?

6. How is the Greek island of Kerkyra better known?

7. In which other country does London stand on the River Thames?

8. Which large river bisects Venezuela?

9. In which European capital is the Atomium monument?

10. What is the county town of Rutland?

11. Which New Zealand island is the third largest in size?

12. What down under is a willy-willy?

13. Which lake do Austria, Germany and Switzerland border?

14. Which is nearer to London, Stockholm or Warsaw?

15. What covers almost half of Canada?

16. Which lighthouse lies off Land's End in Cornwall?

QUIZ 270

① Vesper, Elektra and Christmas are all what?

② Who was arrested on the SS *Montrose* in 1910?

③ What is the greater volume, 8 gallons or 1 bushel?

④ Which French town is famous for its nougat?

⑤ Which footballer was given an honorary knighthood in 1997?

⑥ Horse and Fan are types of what shellfish?

⑦ To which US state are the Bahamas closest?

⑧ Who won more Grand Slam titles, Boris Becker or John McEnroe?

⑨ 'Leaving On A Jet Plane' was whose almost prophetic hit song?

⑩ What does the name of the Belgian city of Bruges mean?

⑪ Whose vice-president was Nelson Rockefeller?

⑫ Where is David Livingstone buried?

⑬ Which word can go after top and before trick?

⑭ In what sport did England's Nigel Boocock excel?

⑮ Chateauneuf du Pape comes from which wine region?

⑯ What was James Callaghan's first name?

QUIZ 271

① What is the BBC's principal orchestra?

② How many flags on a rugby union pitch?

③ What was the capital of Pakistan from 1959 to 1969?

④ Which actress 'breast feeds' David Walliams in *Little Britain*?

⑤ Who wrote the comic opera *The Daughter of the Regiment*?

⑥ What are administrative regions in France called?

⑦ What cocktail is made of rye whiskey, sweet vermouth and bitters?

⑧ Which British explorer translated the *Kama Sutra*?

⑨ What comes next: 'Du vin, du pain, du . . . ' ?

⑩ Who was known as the 'Scourge of God'?

⑪ If you are phobophobic what are you afraid of?

⑫ In which 1979 film did Sting make his big screen debut?

⑬ Add the sporting surname: Irfan and Yusuf . . .

⑭ What in German military circles was a *pickelhaube*?

⑮ When it's noon at GMT, what time is it in Vancouver?

⑯ What is the square root of 625?

QUIZ 272

① How many players are there in an American football team?

② How many Popes were there in 1978?

③ Who is known as 'Muscles from Brussels'?

④ Did Matthew Pinsent row for Oxford or Cambridge?

⑤ In 2008 Russia and South Ossetia fought which country?

⑥ Along which sea is the Barbary Coast?

⑦ Which French prime minister was nicknamed 'Tiger'?

⑧ What is the hardest substance known to man?

⑨ Tsingtao is which country's most popular beer?

⑩ Which couple produced a son called Caesarion?

⑪ What sport features in the 1963 film *This Sporting Life*?

⑫ What was Disney's first non-animation film?

⑬ And who played Jim Hawkins in it?

⑭ Who did Honor Blackman play in the TV series *The Avengers*?

⑮ What word can precede cloth, fire and water?

⑯ Which country did the USA invade in 1983?

QUIZ 273

1. Who is the patron saint of Paris?

2. What nationality was Dr Crippen?

3. What colour are the seats in the House of Lords?

4. A toper consumes what to excess?

5. How many strings on a concert harp?

6. Peter Shilton played his 1000th league game for which club?

7. When was Westminster Abbey founded: 860, 960 or 1060?

8. Who succeeded Stalin as leader of the Soviet Union?

9. What colour is the food dye annatto?

10. Which is the furthest south, Baghdad, Cairo or Tehran?

11. What made its first appearance on Soviet TV in 1988?

12. On what Scottish island are the Callanish Stones?

13. Which husband and wife served in the New Labour government?

14. To what family of birds does the jay belong?

15. Big Daddy is a character in which Tennessee Williams play?

16. Which former England Test cricket captain was born in Peru?

QUIZ 274

① How many international hat-tricks did Jimmy Greaves score?

② In which city was Emma Watson born?

③ Which couple in Greek mythology waited 20 years to be reunited?

④ How many shillings was a crown worth?

⑤ What Christmas song has a dental theme?

⑥ If you are suffering from otalgia, what do you have?

⑦ Who does a hagiographer write about?

⑧ Where was Robert Bunsen, inventor of the burner, born?

⑨ What Shakespeare play has the line: 'Knock, knock, who's there?'?

⑩ Who became the England football manager in 1996?

⑪ What is Berlin's best-known park?

⑫ The banking term CHAPS stands for what?

⑬ What was the Roman name for Ireland?

⑭ Xizang Zizhiqu to the Chinese, what is it called in the West?

⑮ What spilled eleven million gallons of oil in Alaska?

⑯ Which Parsons was a legendary Hollywood gossip columnist?

QUIZ 275

① Who plays Fusilier Dave Tucker in *Soldier Soldier*?

② What happens when hydrogen burns in the air?

③ In *Ghost*, what was the Patrick Swayze character's ex-job?

④ Which US actor made a posthumous TV anti-smoking advert?

⑤ Who traditionally makes and sells candles?

⑥ What is the Japanese parliament called?

⑦ Which archaeological 'find' was unearthed in 1922?

⑧ Who do Rastafarians regard as the manifestation of God?

⑨ '7 O'Clock News/Silent Night' was whose 1966 hit?

⑩ What was the French Resistance in World War Two called?

⑪ In which country was actress Julie Christie born?

⑫ Who was the last man on the moon?

⑬ Whose first novel was *Ghostwritten*?

⑭ Which record-breaking Czech striker was once a goalkeeper?

⑮ What is a throstle?

⑯ How old was Adolf Hitler when he died?

QUIZ 276
SPORT

1. Who won the first women's Rugby World Cup Sevens in 2009?

2. How old was Charlotte Edwards when she made her Test debut?

3. Add the sporting surname: Frank and Ronald . . .

4. What is the longest-running trophy in international sport?

5. Which champion jockey shot himself in 1886 at the age of 29?

6. Which former All Blacks captain was knighted in 1999?

7. Who did Dundee United beat in the 2010 Scottish Cup final?

8. Which sport features in the 1993 film *Cool Runnings*?

9. Where were the last Olympics before The Great War staged?

10. How many first class hundreds did Graham Hick score?

11. In which golf Open does the victor win his weight in cheese?

12. Who captained England most times: Bobby Moore or Billy Wright?

13. In which sport do players compete for the Leonard Trophy?

14. How many times did Nick Faldo win the US Masters?

15. What do the initials stand for in A B de Villiers?

16. Which top NZ Formula One driver never won a grand prix?

QUIZ 277

① Whose autobiography was subtitled: *Don't Tell Kath*?

② Christopher Sly is a character in which Shakespeare play?

③ In which year did Saddam Hussein become Iraq's president?

④ Who took over from Jimmy Young on Radio 2?

⑤ What is the chemical symbol for lead?

⑥ How many islands are there in the Seychelles archipelago?

⑦ Who became Archbishop of York in 2005?

⑧ On a plant, what are the corolla?

⑨ Which 19th-century Scottish writer said: 'Wine is bottled poetry'?

⑩ Mt Elbert is which US mountain range's highest peak?

⑪ Which British prime minister was assassinated in 1812?

⑫ Who commanded the Prussian army at Waterloo in 1815?

⑬ Which US sex research scientist was the subject of a 2004 film?

⑭ How old was the Queen when Prince Edward was born?

⑮ Which political leader did Nguyen Tat Thanh become?

⑯ Bangladesh was formerly what?

QUIZ 278

① Name the economist John Kenneth . . .

② How is Hearst Castle in California also known?

③ Where was Barack Obama born?

④ Herpetology is a study of what?

⑤ What foodstuff is starch from the pith of a palm stem?

⑥ The Glomma is which European country's longest river?

⑦ Who was the narrator in the Scorsese film *The Age of Innocence*?

⑧ What new UK government was formed in 1935?

⑨ Which UK prime minister wrote the novel *Vivian Grey*?

⑩ What was introduced on to London streets in 1961?

⑪ In which country was the French writer Albert Camus born?

⑫ Which new US television drama series took off in 2011?

⑬ What in film-making does a foley artist do?

⑭ Music played between the acts of a play or opera is called what?

⑮ Who in 1990 became Ireland's first woman president?

⑯ What is the alcoholic ingredient in a Snowball cocktail?

QUIZ 279

① Who played the title role in TV's *Father Ted*?

② Which cricketer called his autobiography *MCC*?

③ What undesirable hit list did Burt Reynolds get on to in 2009?

④ What is the largest county in Wales?

⑤ Which two languages are written on the Rosetta Stone?

⑥ What age was Britain's oldest Olympic gold-medal winner?

⑦ And for which sport was the medal won?

⑧ In which century did the Renaissance begin, spreading knowledge and culture from Italy throughout Europe?

⑨ What are the New Hebrides now called?

⑩ Who declined the English crown in 1657?

⑪ What is a female wolf called?

⑫ Which UK industry was nationalized in 1967?

⑬ Name the Chancellor of the Exchequer who resigned in 1989.

⑭ Which US religious leader's real name was George Baker?

⑮ When was the English pound note withdrawn?

⑯ Who did Ian McShane play in the TV series *Deadwood*?

QUIZ 280

① Who was the UK's first woman foreign secretary?

② What is the name of the Matt Lucas/David Walliams airline spoof?

③ Who was British flat-racing champion jockey a record 26 times?

④ What is a small zoo called?

⑤ In the Bible what follows the First Book of Kings?

⑥ Which food writer's book was *An Omelette and a Glass of Wine*?

⑦ The Bass Strait separates which two areas of land?

⑧ Where in 1914 was the world's first traffic light installed?

⑨ How is the Northrop Grumman B-2 Spirit better known?

⑩ Who was prime minister in Britain's last Liberal government?

⑪ What is the Italian word for a winery?

⑫ *The Room* was whose first play?

⑬ What nationality is FIFA president Sepp Blatter?

⑭ The Punic Wars were fought between Rome and who?

⑮ Who wrote *The Naked Lunch*?

⑯ What is another name for rappelling?

QUIZ 281

① What was the mascot of the 2011 Cricket World Cup?

② Who was lead vocalist for The Kinks?

③ What make of car is Latin for 'I hear'?

④ Who played Mr Orange in the film *Reservoir Dogs*?

⑤ What word was removed from decimal coins in 1982?

⑥ What percentage of Egypt is desert?

⑦ How many points are awarded for a dropped goal in rugby league?

⑧ In which ship did Francis Drake circumnavigate the world?

⑨ What did the Romans call *plumbum*?

⑩ All the Lancastrian kings had what name?

⑪ What is the US rugby team known as?

⑫ How many O-levels did John Major leave school with?

⑬ Which rank is more senior, lieutenant general or major general?

⑭ What sort of energy is sourced from hot springs?

⑮ Dennis Brain was a noted soloist on which musical instrument?

⑯ What is Gaelic for 'cheers'?

QUIZ 282

① Which women's tennis player tested positive for cocaine in 2007?

② Who is the patron saint of Edinburgh?

③ Which US president said: 'The buck stops here'?

④ Colin Myler was which publication's last editor?

⑤ Which French artist was born first, Manet or Monet?

⑥ Who once used an aluminium bat in a Test match?

⑦ What is the symbol of the US Democratic Party?

⑧ Who was called the 'Hammer of the Scots'?

⑨ Which jockey was nicknamed 'The Long Fellow'?

⑩ Bryan Adams sang 'When You're Gone' with Mel C and who else?

⑪ Which Chinese desert is known as the 'Sea of Death'?

⑫ In how many years will the sun run out of fuel?

⑬ Where is the European Investment Bank?

⑭ Which two countries play for the Worrell Trophy?

⑮ What did Australia celebrate in 1988?

⑯ Which king launched the Spanish Armada of 1588?

QUIZ 283

① What is the gestation period of a kangaroo?

② Bearded d'Uccle, Red Shaver and Vorwerk are all breeds of what?

③ Which two 20th-century US presidents were Quakers?

④ What is a philargyrist?

⑤ Which cricketing country played its first Test match in 1889?

⑥ Mercury combined with another metal is called what?

⑦ What is the capital of Rwanda?

⑧ Which couturier started life as Gabrielle Bonheur?

⑨ Who murdered John Lennon?

⑩ What are congruent lines?

⑪ Which Beatle sang backing vocals on Donovan's 'Mellow Yellow'?

⑫ In which country was the aerosol can invented?

⑬ Where is Plymouth Rock?

⑭ The initials of the French football club PSG stand for what?

⑮ What is Israel's official currency?

⑯ How long did Edward VIII reign?

QUIZ 284
CINEMA & TV

(1) In *Minder*, what is Arthur Daley's favourite watering hole?

(2) With what film did Robert Redford make his directorial debut?

(3) What is the name of Rigsby's cat in *Rising Damp*?

(4) Who was first choice for the title role in *Shakespeare in Love*?

(5) What song wakes up Bill Murray in *Groundhog Day*?

(6) Add the number in the film title: . . . *Heads in a Duffell Bag*.

(7) Rodney Trotter has GCSEs in which two subjects?

(8) Who is Matt Lucas in Tim Burton's film *Alice in Wonderland*?

(9) Who was the original chairman of BBC's *Question Time*?

(10) Which TV series spun off from *Z Cars*?

(11) How many boxes are there to open in *Deal or No Deal*?

(12) Which film role do Peter Cushing and Robert Downey Jr share?

(13) In which Bond film is Honey Ryder a character?

(14) Can you name Hyacinth Bucket's three sisters?

(15) Who directed the films *Revolutionary Road* and *Road to Perdition*?

(16) Who is Brian's wife in *New Tricks*?

QUIZ 285

① What is the effect of a nitrogen embolism?

② Which 20th-century US president was born on the Fourth of July?

③ Where would you find a reagent bottle?

④ What is a French cheese shop called?

⑤ Which jazz musician fell to his death from a hotel window in 1988?

⑥ After which famous explorer is Venice's airport named?

⑦ Which Italian prime minister was a former singer on cruise ships?

⑧ By what name was the 17th-century zealot Matthew Hopkins known?

⑨ In *My Week with Marilyn* who plays Monroe?

⑩ The Beatles song 'Baby You're A Rich Man' is dedicated to whom?

⑪ Which former German football player coached Scotland?

⑫ Which, in 1978, was the first country to ban harmful aerosols?

⑬ In which year was the microwave oven invented?

⑭ What word can come before bath, less and sport?

⑮ Who was younger on Bond debut, Daniel Craig or Sean Connery?

⑯ From which country did Panama secede in 1903?

QUIZ 286

① Who was the fifth actor to play Dr Who on television?

② Which English king introduced the 12-man jury system?

③ The elephant and rhinoceros are what sort of animal?

④ What are dartboards traditionally made of?

⑤ Which former wife of Sean Connery died in 2011?

⑥ In which country was Rosa Luxemburg a communist revolutionary?

⑦ What is a personal representative of the Pope called?

⑧ What was Pierce Brosnan's first Bond movie?

⑨ Which sport involves a rock, house and sheet?

⑩ What Bobby Darin song combined Christmas and New Year?

⑪ Which British boxer struck the gong for J Arthur Rank films?

⑫ Which curly redhead started life as a comic strip?

⑬ What can be a compliment or the price of peace?

⑭ In the fashion world, what is an 'LBD'?

⑮ Which golfer made plus fours the on-course fashion?

⑯ What stuffed Heston Blumenthal's Fat Duck restaurant in 2009?

QUIZ 287

① What was Richard Branson's first business venture?

② Who invented the wind-up radio?

③ Who won a British cycling title at the age of 54?

④ What does the word 'eureka' mean?

⑤ Which US defence secretary was given an honorary knighthood?

⑥ Jimmy Porter is the central character in which iconic play?

⑦ What flour is traditionally used to make blinis?

⑧ Which European country gave women the right to vote in 1971?

⑨ Kate Winslet won the 2009 'Best Actress' Oscar for which film?

⑩ What is the capital of Slovakia?

⑪ How many movements are there in Gustav Holst's *Planets Suite*?

⑫ Who was born at 17 Bruton Street, Mayfair, in 1926?

⑬ What is a macaroni when it isn't a pasta?

⑭ How many years of marriage make a platinum anniversary?

⑮ What is the name of the dog in *Three Men in a Boat*?

⑯ Which country is credited with inventing the wheel?

QUIZ 288

① Which two countries went to war in 1969 after a football match?

② What is the official newspaper of record in England?

③ Which explorer opened the first sea route to India?

④ In the 2008 film, Iron Man is whose alter ego?

⑤ What colour caps do water polo goalkeepers wear?

⑥ How many children did Johann Sebastian Bach have?

⑦ What machine is used to process raw cotton?

⑧ In the song, which river is 'wider than a mile'?

⑨ How many times does the number 9 appear between 1 and 100?

⑩ What is the largest member of the antelope family?

⑪ Cetology is the study of what?

⑫ What is the gestation period of a rabbit?

⑬ Complete the film title: *Cook, the Thief, His Wife and* . . .

⑭ What is the main town on the island of Skye?

⑮ Who led the first crossing of Antarctica in 1958?

⑯ What is the world's longest-running sailing regatta?

QUIZ 289

① Where was the Queen educated?

② Who was New York's mayor at the time of 9/11?

③ What USSR foreign minister lent his name to an improvised weapon?

④ Who plays Velvet in the 1978 film *International Velvet*?

⑤ What is the regulation height and width of a football goal?

⑥ To which Scottish island were the contestants in *Castaway* sent?

⑦ How many points are there on the crown of the Statue of Liberty?

⑧ And what do they represent?

⑨ Who drove Mary Jo Kopechne to her death in 1969?

⑩ A female singing voice in the middle range is a what?

⑪ Where is the world's first 'seven star' hotel?

⑫ In Greek mythology, Thalia was the muse of what?

⑬ Who was Elton John's long-time lyricist?

⑭ Which countries formed the Triple Entente in World War One?

⑮ Who did Jacqui Smith follow as Home Secretary?

⑯ Michael Sheen's father was a professional lookalike of whom?

QUIZ 290

① What crowned Elizabeth II?

② What is the world's largest museum and research centre?

③ And where is it?

④ What does a cynologist study?

⑤ Who painted the gold and silver portrait of Adele Bloch-Bauer I?

⑥ Which French player was sent off in the 1998 FIFA World Cup final?

⑦ Who was Margaret Thatcher's controversial economic adviser?

⑧ Which football club does Fat Boy Slim have a stake in?

⑨ Hitchcock's film *The Birds* is based on a short story by whom?

⑩ Zealand is which country's biggest island?

⑪ Whose autobiography was called *Dreams From My Father*?

⑫ Who commanded the British forces in Burma in World War Two?

⑬ TV 'Dragon' Hilary Devey has made her money in which industry?

⑭ How many BRITS did Michael Jackson win?

⑮ What singer got married on Johnny Carson's *Tonight Show* in 1969?

⑯ What did the comet Shoemaker-Levy 9 collide with in 1994?

QUIZ 291
SCIENCE & NATURE

① Chromatics is the science of what?

② *Lunokhod 1* was the USSR's first what?

③ Which insect has the shortest life?

④ What is the chemical symbol for mercury?

⑤ 'Planet' comes from a Greek word meaning what?

⑥ If you are genophobic what are you afraid of?

⑦ What is an enzyme?

⑧ Who is most famous for his last theorem?

⑨ How many noble gasses are there?

⑩ What flower's name in Greek means 'rose tree'?

⑪ What is a fibrous band that connects muscle to bone?

⑫ What does a hygrometer measure?

⑬ How does a lamprey feed?

⑭ What followed the Triassic period?

⑮ The opossum belongs to what animal group?

⑯ What, geologically speaking, is an aiguille?

QUIZ 292

① What is a model of excellence or perfection?

② What Greek goddess was associated with witchcraft and magic?

③ Who was the first black West Indian to play cricket for England?

④ Larimar, Sodalite and Aventurine are all types of what?

⑤ Which British TV soap was first aired in 1992?

⑥ Which is the largest of the Florida Keys?

⑦ In which country was the emperor called the 'Son of Heaven'?

⑧ Which boxer does Russell Crowe play in *Cinderella Man*?

⑨ The first BRIT awards marked which milestone event?

⑩ What game is the forerunner of ice hockey?

⑪ DCMG stands for what decoration?

⑫ Whose autobiography was self-deprecatingly called *Dear Fatty*?

⑬ What flower is associated with vanity and egoism?

⑭ Which one of the cricketing Bedser twins died in 2006?

⑮ Whose mistress was Clara Petacci?

⑯ Alfred Jingle is a character in which Charles Dickens novel?

QUIZ 293

① Which UK university has the most students?

② What colour is the diamond shape on the Brazilian flag?

③ In Internet chat, what does OTOH stand for?

④ For which film did Audrey Hepburn win her only Oscar?

⑤ Who was the youngest member of England's 1966 World Cup team?

⑥ Where in Italy was the great earthquake of 2009?

⑦ What sporting trophy went missing for seven days in 1966?

⑧ Which German chancellor won the Nobel Peace Prize in 1971?

⑨ What did The Four Aims change their name to?

⑩ Frederick and Gabriella are which royal couple's children?

⑪ Who is the First Lord of the Treasury?

⑫ What is the symbol of the US Republican Party?

⑬ Which Quinnell won most rugby caps for Wales: Derek or Scott?

⑭ The film *All the King's Men* was based on whose novel?

⑮ Which comedy-writing duo created 'The Glums'?

⑯ In which year was nylon invented: 1927 or 1937?

QUIZ 294

① What is the process for strengthening rubber?

② Which prime minister introduced the Open University?

③ What does the debilitating disease ME stand for?

④ How many eyes has a bee?

⑤ Against which country did Steven Finn make his Test debut?

⑥ Which is the fastest swimming bird?

⑦ Whose first film as director was *Oh What a Lovely War*?

⑧ Which 1815 congress redefined Europe after Napoleon's defeat?

⑨ Where are Sir Stanley Matthews' ashes interred?

⑩ Which is New Zealand's larger island, North or South?

⑪ What is improvised jazz singing called?

⑫ Where in the USA is the Rock and Roll Hall of Fame?

⑬ When it is not a badger's home what is a sett?

⑭ What is another name for a Gregorian chant?

⑮ In 1849 Elizabeth Blackwell became the USA's first female what?

⑯ What is the meeting of two rivers called?

QUIZ 295

① What is Spanish for 'prawns'?

② The theme tune for *The Office* is a version of which song?

③ Obsession, Euphoria and Eternity are perfumes from whom?

④ What is the name of Dennis the Menace's dog?

⑤ Where was the first science museum opened in 1752?

⑥ Who left the Rolling Stones in 1992?

⑦ Which UK football club's home ground is the Madejski Stadium?

⑧ What have you found with a *mot juste*?

⑨ How many times did Ross in *Friends* get divorced?

⑩ What is a Dandie Dinmont?

⑪ On which river is the city of Cork?

⑫ The art of knotting string or chord in patterns is called what?

⑬ Which chemical element is named after a Scottish village?

⑭ In which country is the Serengeti National Park?

⑮ What is a wadi?

⑯ What band did Madonna and Dan Gilroy form?

QUIZ 296

① Who is Ricky Gervais' character in *The Office*?

② Why did Brian Lara call his first child Sydney?

③ What is the fossilized resin of extinct conifers?

④ How many gills are there in a pint?

⑤ Whose political memoir is titled *A Journey*?

⑥ Which US actor had a starring role in the TV series *Colditz*?

⑦ What is England's greatest constitutional document?

⑧ Cape Blanc, Africa's most northerly point, is in which country?

⑨ What does an EEG machine measure?

⑩ Which Welsh rugby player was known as 'The King'?

⑪ What is the technical term for a lie detector?

⑫ Who did George W Bush defeat in the 2004 presidential election?

⑬ What was the name of Bill Haley's group?

⑭ Anthony Quinn was which famous film director's son-in-law?

⑮ Which African river did Mungo Park chart?

⑯ Which West England club made its Football League debut in 2003?

QUIZ 297

1. What emblem was the symbol of the French monarchy?

2. Who wrote the opera *The Tender Land*?

3. Pre euro, Germany's currency consisted of the mark and what else?

4. How many days does the Venice Carnival last?

5. Was the writer Richmal Crompton male or female?

6. The Durand Line is the border between which two countries?

7. Bulawayo, as in the Zimbabwean town, means what?

8. Molluscs with a hinged shell are called what?

9. Who was America named after?

10. Which Swedish actress did Sammy Davis Jr marry in 1961?

11. Glevum was the Roman name for which English city?

12. Which US film's dialogue was in Aramaic, Latin and Hebrew?

13. What type of art exhibit uniquely won the 2010 Turner Prize?

14. Name the US film director: David Wark . . .

15. Luik is the Flemish name for which Belgian city?

16. How old would Elvis Presley have been in 2010?

QUIZ 298

① Which fraudulent operation pays investors with their own money?

② What country is known as the 'Roof of the World'?

③ Which 'royal' escaped a kidnap attempt in 1974?

④ What prefix indicates a 'billionth'?

⑤ Dizzy, Old Fashioned and Collins are all types of what?

⑥ When did Mt Vesuvius last erupt: 1944, 1954 or 1964?

⑦ Who was the first black recipient of the Nobel Peace Prize?

⑧ In which novel by Franz Kafka is Joseph K the main character?

⑨ Which 'New Wave' French film director died in 1984?

⑩ Who is Scotland's premier non-royal duke?

⑪ What safety device did Walter Hunt invent in 1849?

⑫ Complete the film title: *The . . . Maguires*

⑬ What modern proverb concerns an overweight female chanteuse?

⑭ What is the world's largest library?

⑮ By what other name is Holy Island known?

⑯ What was the US equivalent of the NAAFI?

QUIZ 299
MUSIC

① *Dig Out Your Soul* was whose final album?

② Berlioz, Gounod and Schumann all composed works about whom?

③ 'Lady Marmalade' was a 1974 hit for which group?

④ Who founded the MOBOs: Kanya King or Kanye West?

⑤ In which Richard Gere film was Blondie's 'Call Me' featured?

⑥ What was Taylor Swift's 2006 debut album called?

⑦ Lou Reed and Metallica's 2011 album is called what?

⑧ Which character in *Les Miserables* sings 'I Dreamed A Dream'?

⑨ Who had another hit with 'Oops! I Did It Again'?

⑩ What 1990s song became the theme for Boots' TV commercials?

⑪ Which distinguished producer won a BRIT in 1984?

⑫ 'My Funny Valentine': music by Richard Rodgers, lyrics by whom?

⑬ 'Love Is All Around' by Wet Wet Wet is in which 1994 film?

⑭ Who recorded 'Relight My Fire' with Take That in 1993?

⑮ Who wrote the music for *Billy Elliot the Musical*?

⑯ Who is known as the 'Mod Father'?

QUIZ 300

① In what country would you drink beer out of a 'middy'?

② What word can come before biscuits, bottle and colour?

③ What is 66°33'N?

④ In what year was Barack Obama born?

⑤ I'M THE KILLER is an anagram of which great cricketer's name?

⑥ What was the theme song from the film *Top Gun*?

⑦ And who sang it on the soundtrack?

⑧ Where in the US is there a highway with 26 lanes?

⑨ What two spirits go into a Singapore Sling?

⑩ Which US jazz virtuoso was blind?

⑪ Whose voice was Stinky Pete in *Toy Story* 2?

⑫ Barkis is a character in which Charles Dickens novel?

⑬ Which major underground cave was discovered in England in 2006?

⑭ In karate, what is senior of the two ranks for contestants?

⑮ What is the oldest living language still spoken in Europe?

⑯ Which country's international car registration is HR?

QUIZ 301

① Who is older, Angela Merkel or Nicholas Sarkozy?

② Who is the second-in-command of a merchant ship?

③ Who went from AC Milan to Real Madrid for €65m in 2009?

④ Psephology is a statistical study of what?

⑤ Which George's real name was Amandine Aurore Lucile Dupin?

⑥ Pepinex and Telegraph are varieties of which salad item?

⑦ Who plays Victor Laszlo in the film *Casablanca*?

⑧ What was the Internet music service launched in 1999?

⑨ Who did Lyndon Johnson beat in the 1964 US presidential election?

⑩ Which pretender to the English throne was hanged in 1499?

⑪ What is the common name for magnesium silicate hydroxide?

⑫ Who was Zimbabwe's first president?

⑬ What is a young grouse called?

⑭ Queen Maud Land is on which continent?

⑮ What is England's second largest natural lake?

⑯ Who said: 'The report of my death was an exaggeration'?

QUIZ 302

① Against whom did Alastair Cook make his Test debut in 2006?

② David Cameron is the youngest prime minister since who in 1812?

③ Where was the Great English Earthquake of 1884?

④ An otolaryngologist is a medical specialist in what?

⑤ The Notre Dame shift is a manoeuvre in which sport?

⑥ A dithyramb was a song or poem in honour of which Greek god?

⑦ Which religious leader's chief residence was the Potala Palace?

⑧ Which 19th-century workers opposed the mechanization of weaving?

⑨ In which country was Australian prime minster Julia Gillard born?

⑩ What type of conveyance is a luge?

⑪ Who are Mike D, MCA and Ad-Rock?

⑫ What is an angle more than 90° called?

⑬ Which former spy spilled some of the beans in *My Silent War*?

⑭ How many non-royal Knights of the Garter are there at any one time?

⑮ Which town in Tuscany gives its name to a white marble?

⑯ Whose last words were: 'That was a great game of golf, fellas.'?

QUIZ 303

① Who was the first footballer to cost £15 million?

② Which member of the British royal family died in May 1972?

③ Who wrote the short story *Three-Ten to Yuma*?

④ What is a kylie?

⑤ The pa'anga is which country's official currency?

⑥ How and where did cross-Channel swimmer Captain Webb die?

⑦ In *La Bohème*, who does Rudolfo fall in love with?

⑧ What is the collective name for crocodiles?

⑨ Which famous German menswear label made Nazi uniforms?

⑩ In which country were The Cheeky Girls born?

⑪ A0, A7 and A8 are all what?

⑫ Who was appointed England rugby coach in 1988?

⑬ Who was the first German chancellor to visit Israel?

⑭ In Greek mythology, who decapitated the many-headed Hydra?

⑮ When was the MCC founded: 1767, 1777, 1787?

⑯ Which British architect designed the new Madrid airport?

QUIZ 304

① What colour is zero on a roulette wheel?

② Which organization's motto is 'Blood and Fire'?

③ K is the chemical symbol for what?

④ What 'ology' monitors the spread and control of diseases?

⑤ Which rugby union position does not exist in rugby league?

⑥ Grice, Quatrefoil and Volant are all terms of what?

⑦ How did Viv Stanshall of The Bonzo Dog Doo-Dah Band die in 1995?

⑧ In which country was Greenpeace founded?

⑨ And where is the organization's international headquarters?

⑩ Which is the only US state with a royal palace?

⑪ Who plays David Horton in *The Vicar of Dibley*?

⑫ Arnhem Land is a region in which Australian state?

⑬ For which film did John Mills win his only Oscar?

⑭ How many singles titles did Martina Navratilova win?

⑮ What is the ICA?

⑯ How was Martha Jane Cannary better known?

QUIZ 305

① Mt Parnassus was home to which Greek god?

② Dodransbicentennial celebrates how many years?

③ Add the showbiz surname: Richard and Karen . . .

④ What nationality is UN secretary-general Ban Ki-moon?

⑤ Which water creature shares its name with a Florida river?

⑥ At which Olympics did Steve Redgrave win his first gold medal?

⑦ Where is the HQ of the International Monetary Fund?

⑧ What is the French name for Aachen?

⑨ Hausa, Igbo and Yoruba are ethnic groups of which African country?

⑩ What is the basket used to propel the ball in pelote called?

⑪ Who wrote the screenplay for the film *The Servant*?

⑫ Around which year did the Black Death wipe out 30 to 60% of the population of Europe?

⑬ Which major record company rejected The Beatles in 1962?

⑭ What is the chemical symbol for arsenic?

⑮ Who played Jessica Lovejoy in *The Simpsons*?

⑯ Who was Archbishop of Canterbury at the time of the Abdication?

QUIZ 306

① What animal trio is Mizaru, Mikazaru and Mazaru?

② In which US state is Harvard University?

③ What were Jaguar cars called before World War Two?

④ Which liquid gallon is larger, UK or USA?

⑤ On a clothing care label what does a crossed out circle denote?

⑥ Which US TV evangelist's fling with a call girl took him off-air?

⑦ What is 'Indiana' Jones' first name?

⑧ Which country did Olympic champion Betty Cuthbert represent?

⑨ In which film is Travis Bickle the disturbed central character?

⑩ What in medical terms is a syncope?

⑪ Which Asian country's currency is the Taka?

⑫ Who composed the symphony entitled *Babi Yar*?

⑬ Which is the UK's third largest city in terms of population?

⑭ What do Americans call a notepad?

⑮ What is a watertight load-bearing wall in a ship's hull called?

⑯ What is the road to Hell paved with?

QUIZ 307
HISTORY

① Where was Bonnie Prince Charlie born in 1720?

② How did Herman Goering die?

③ Whose 'Rivers of Blood' speech created great controversy?

④ In which year did Sir Winston Churchill die?

⑤ Which member of the royal family died in an air crash in 1942?

⑥ Who was the victorious Red Army commander at Stalingrad?

⑦ Which war ended in 1905?

⑧ What does the S stand for in George S Patton?

⑨ Which leader of the French Revolution was guillotined in 1794?

⑩ Who was the Apache chief who died in 1909?

⑪ In which country was Lenin when the Russian Revolution began?

⑫ Who was the most famous of the Spanish conquistadors?

⑬ Which dictator did Saloth Sar become?

⑭ Which US president was assassinated in 1881?

⑮ What was the US equivalent of the British 'Tommy'?

⑯ Who became French president in 1981?

QUIZ 308

① What is two dozen times four score?

② The site of the Babi Yar massacres is near which city?

③ Which US theatrical awards are named after Antoinette Perry?

④ What is 'digamy'?

⑤ Malachite is what colour?

⑥ What SF writer has an asteroid and a Mars crater named after him?

⑦ Which US comedian and actor was born Joseph Levitch?

⑧ What was the first credit card?

⑨ When did Greece join the European Community?

⑩ What is the least populous state in the USA?

⑪ Foreign ambassadors to the UK are accredited to what?

⑫ What is Graham Greene's novel *Stamboul Train* titled in the USA?

⑬ What did Dmitri Mendeleyev classify in 1869?

⑭ In which year did Band Aid produce their first Christmas record?

⑮ What strait separates Anglesey from the Welsh mainland?

⑯ Which US jockey was called 'The Kentucky Kid'?

QUIZ 309

① What, at sea, did the initials RMS stand for?

② Where are OPEC's headquarters?

③ What are also known as 'equatorial calms'?

④ Where did the first industrial revolution take place?

⑤ Whose catchphrase was: 'It's the way I tell 'em.'?

⑥ On which river does Dublin stand?

⑦ Who did Sirhan Bissara Sirhan kill in 1968?

⑧ What is the name for the current era in Japan, Heisei or Shōwa?

⑨ Which US state is known as the 'Garden State'?

⑩ 'Christmas Is Just Around The Corner' was a 2008 hit for whom?

⑪ Which Italian racing driver died at Monaco in 1967?

⑫ In the film *About a Boy* who plays the boy in question?

⑬ And on whose novel was the film based?

⑭ From which country does raga music come?

⑮ Who designed the aviary at the London Zoo?

⑯ FL on a number plate indicates which country of origin?

QUIZ 310

① A vespiary is home to which insect?

② THAT GREAT CHARMER is an anagram of which politician's name?

③ If you are agliophobic what are you afraid of?

④ China took over Macao from which country?

⑤ What is the media and entertainment industry's trade union?

⑥ Who did Neil Kinnock beat in the 1983 Labour leadership contest?

⑦ Where did David Mitchell and Robert Webb first perform together?

⑧ What does 'vulpine' mean?

⑨ In which film does Bette Davis play Mrs Van Schuyler?

⑩ What is the world's highest waterfall?

⑪ And in which country is it?

⑫ How many kilograms in a quintal?

⑬ Derby, Pelham and Russell have all been what?

⑭ What is a Russian tea urn called?

⑮ Who directed the 2006 film *United 93*?

⑯ Which British tennis player reached the final of the 1977 Australian Open?

QUIZ 311

① Where was the world's first duty free shop?

② What was used to kill Leon Trotsky in 1940?

③ How much does one carat weigh?

④ In which village was Dr Finlay a GP?

⑤ How old was Macaulay Culkin when he made *Home Alone*?

⑥ What animals pull the god Thor's wagon across the sky?

⑦ Which comedy duo started out as PE teachers?

⑧ What does the name Fitzroy mean?

⑨ Who wrote the patriotic song 'Keep The Home Fires Burning'?

⑩ In what sport is the ball called a 'sliotar'?

⑪ Who is the patron saint of broadcasters?

⑫ Ununoctium, krypton and xenon are all what?

⑬ Madame de Pompadour was mistress of which French king?

⑭ What was the former capital of Spain?

⑮ Add the fraternal sporting surname: Graeme and Peter...

⑯ What navigational instrument measures longitude and latitude?

QUIZ 312

① What is the meteorological term for rain, snow and hail?

② In which game might you launch an 'Austrian attack'?

③ Who was the first to win an Oscar for 'Best Actress'?

④ What is the better part of valour?

⑤ Which 'minor country' beat West Indies in the 1996 World Cup?

⑥ With which international airline did BA merge in 2010?

⑦ *E pluribus unum* is which country's motto?

⑧ And what does it mean?

⑨ When was London's Metropolitan Police founded: 1819, 1829, 1839?

⑩ Who was the last of the 1960s 'Rat Pack' to die?

⑪ What does *ibid* mean?

⑫ Who was the founder of child psychoanalysis?

⑬ Which seagull did Neil Diamond make a song about?

⑭ When was Joan of Arc canonized: 1720, 1820 or 1920?

⑮ Which sport featured in the 1992 film *White Men Can't Jump*?

⑯ Which two African states merged to become Tanzania?

QUIZ 313

1. What does the academic term *alma mater* literally mean?

2. Who was the first US president to have been divorced?

3. Who is the hypnotist in *Little Britain*?

4. How old was Maria Sharapova when Martina Navratilova spotted her?

5. Which scientist became Master of the Mint in 1699?

6. In the proverb, what is sloth the key to?

7. What colour are the seats in the House of Commons?

8. Which group of islands is off the southern tip of South America?

9. St Patrick is the patron saint of which West African country?

10. Which is further south, New Orleans or San Diego?

11. What is a carambola?

12. In which country is the world's largest pyramid?

13. Who plays Bridget Jones' father on screen?

14. In which year did Lenin die?

15. Who wrote the cult 1960s song 'MacArthur Park'?

16. Who famously said: 'In two words, impossible'? – Sam Goldwyn or George W Bush?

QUIZ 314

① What creates pumice stone?

② In the film *The Departed*, who does Jack Nicholson play?

③ What is 377 in Roman numerals?

④ Who did Robert Ford shoot dead in 1882?

⑤ Writer H G Wells' father was a professional in which sport?

⑥ What was the Regency Mrs Fitzherbert's first name?

⑦ The source of the Amazon is in which country?

⑧ Who said that patriotism is 'the last refuge of a scoundrel'?

⑨ Ethel le Neve was the mistress of which murderer?

⑩ The song 'Side By Side By Side' comes from which musical?

⑪ Who won most Test caps, Will Carling or Rory Underwood?

⑫ What was the Blue Riband awarded for?

⑬ Which former Indian cricket captain died in 2011?

⑭ Who was Natasha Kaplinsky's partner in *Strictly Come Dancing*?

⑮ What does the prefix 'aber' in British place names mean?

⑯ How many US states border Alaska?

ANSWERS

QUIZ 1

1. Clement Atlee; 2. Dance; 3. *Canberra*; 4. Sail; 5. Russian salad;
6. Morgiana; 7. Johann Sebastian Bach; 8. Dr Andrei Sakharov; 9. Cousin;
10. Adrian Anthony; 11. Bird; 12. Good news; 13. Five; 14. Oysters
wrapped in bacon; 15. Tony Hatch; 16. Librarian

QUIZ 2

1. Royal College of Music; 2. Word game; 3. Carrow Road; 4. Vengaboys;
5. A fruit and herb cordial; 6. Emily; 7. Nick Hornby's; 8. Nephew;
9. Ten; 10. Leo Tolstoy; 11. Samantha; 12. Two; 13. Mollusc; 14. Parker
and Barrow; 15. Jonas Brothers; 16. Pen

QUIZ 3

1. Huyton; 2. Grand Central (NY); 3. Ringo Starr; 4. Chicken Maryland;
5. Ceres; 6. The Thieving Magpie; 7. Liver; 8. Vince Cable; 9. Ewart;
10. George Cole; 11. 21 June; 12. Al Jolson; 13. Three; 14. Australia;
15. Cressida; 16. Twenty

QUIZ 4

1. Peninsular and Oriental; 2. Lou Costello; 3. Cemetery Lane; 4. The
Pythia; 5. *Great Expectations*; 6. Biafra; 7. Freshwater fish; 8. T S Eliot;
9. Bristol's; 10. Two; 11. Paul Martin; 12. 1984; 13. Bashful; 14. Michael
Ondaatje; 15. Prehistoric cave paintings; 16. 'Advance Australia Fair'

QUIZ 5

1. General Augusto Pinochet; 2. Selfridge's; 3. Bowes-Lyon; 4. Australia;
5. Hairdresser; 6. Double Diamond; 7. C S Forester; 8. The Pobble (in
Edward Lear's poem); 9. George Wallace; 10. Neapolitan (Italian);
11. Peter Sellers; 12. Computer languages; 13. Sebastian Faulks;
14. Electric razor; 15. MCMXXXIX; 16. Bursting with laughter

QUIZ 6

1. Gondola; 2. Lyndon Johnson; 3. Edvard Grieg; 4. January; 5. Chicle, a natural latex product; 6. Cincinnati; 7. Closet; 8. Wassily; 9. Matt Lucas; 10. Jonathan Swift; 11. On a skewer; 12. New York; 13. Napoleon's; 14. Howard Webb; 15. Jane Seymour; 16. Eight

QUIZ 7

1. Albanian; 2. He safely crash-landed his passenger aircraft on New York's Hudson River; 3. 1971; 4. External; 5. Dental plate; 6. Speyside; 7. Potassium nitrate; 8. Cambodia; 9. Bankside power station; 10. Polo; 11. Chinese gooseberries; 12. First Lieutenant; 13. Desert Rats; 14. Bird; 15. M62; 16. *Cosi Fan Tutte*

QUIZ 8 (Sport)

1. England; 2. Eight; 3. Tourist Trophy; 4. Scars; 5. Bristol Rovers; 6. Diane Leather; 7. Crossbow (bolt); 8. Keith Fletcher; 9. Sir Stanley Matthews; 10. 2006 (Hungarian); 11. FA Cup; 12. Five; 13. Flushing Meadows; 14. Two; 15. Boxing; 16. The green

QUIZ 9

1. Roger Hargreaves; 2. Axminster; 3. Time flies; 4. Jimmy Carter; 5. Julienne; 6. Beijing; 7. Former; 8. Typefaces; 9. St Bernadette's; 10. Finchley; 11. Two; 12. Gouda; 13. Empire Service; 14. Telephone; 15. Tucker Jenkins; 16. Ronald Reagan

QUIZ 10

1. Porcelain; 2. John Smith; 3. Fell off his roof; 4. Ewes' milk; 5. Queen Anne's Lace; 6. Stoke Poges (Buckinghamshire); 7. Marathon; 8. Cyanide; 9. 1996; 10. Pisa; 11. Three; 12. Dudley Moore; 13. Joanne Kathleen; 14. Hardness; 15. Robin Cook; 16. Motorcycle racing

QUIZ 11

1. Ready to wear; 2. Scotland; 3. Robusta; 4. Arthur Wellesley;
5. Sherlock Holmes; 6. Romania; 7. Oxfordshire; 8. 1998; 9. Marshal
Pétain; 10. Thomas Harris; 11. Twelve drummers drumming; 12. Leg;
13. Ten; 14. *Trains à grande vitesse*; 15. Douglas Hogg; 16. Renault 4

QUIZ 12

1. Venice; 2. Peter Sutcliffe; 3. *Howard's End*; 4. USA; 5. Norman Mailer;
6. Russian MiG-21; 7. Mediterranean Sea and Red Sea; 8. 112; 9. Rebecca
Loos; 10. St Jude; 11. Aden (now Yemen); 12. *Casino Royale*; 13. Andy
Goldsworthy; 14. *Modus operandi*; 15. Crocodile; 16. The Grand

QUIZ 13

1. Caribbean; 2. Goose; 3. Tyres; 4. *South Pacific*; 5. Hell; 6. Lebanon;
7. Lofted shots; 8. Pier Paolo Pasolini; 9. Alan Alexander; 10. Stevie
Smith; 11. *Morning Cloud*; 12. 1963; 13. Jimmy Carter; 14. Maxwell Reed;
15. 3/4 time; 16. Pointillism

QUIZ 14

1. Los Alamos; 2. Derek Randall; 3. *Id est* (ie that is); 4. 'The Star-Spangled
Banner'; 5. Lancaster and York; 6. Sonny and Cher; 7. Mumbai;
8. Birmingham; 9. Charles De Gaulle; 10. 1948; 11. Bloemfontein;
12. Steve Brookstein; 13. Antifreeze; 14. Dusty Springfield; 15. Isle of
Wight; 16. Terrence

QUIZ 15 (Cinema & TV)

1. *Some Like It Hot*; 2. Vicar of Dibley; 3. Glenn Ford; 4.*The Eiger Sanction*;
5. Ferris and Collier; 6. Dr Jennifer Melfi; 7. White skin; 8. *Florizel Street*;
9. Danny Boyle; 10. Mobile Army Surgical Hospital; 11. Beau; 12. Robbie
Coltrane; 13. Chester; 14. Alfred Hitchcock's; 15. Richard Yates';
16. Patrick McGoohan in *The Prisoner*

QUIZ 16

1. Rhode Island; 2. Dennis Potter; 3. Warlock; 4. George Bernard Shaw; 5. Valerie Harper; 6. Worcestershire's; 7. Prospero; 8. A rood; 9. Emperor penguin; 10. Warlord; 11. Slow tempo; 12. Sheep; 13. Work; 14. John Wyndham; 15. Dadaism; 16. Airline pilot

QUIZ 17

1. St Peter; 2. Edwina Currie; 3. Brazil; 4. Adrian Lyne; 5. Two; 6. Homepride's; 7. The Doughnut; 8. Igor Stravinsky; 9. Bering Sea; 10. Sir Everton Weekes; 11. *La Gioconda*; 12. Booker Prize; 13. Smallpox; 14. Stoat; 15. Carla Bruni; 16. Bristol

QUIZ 18

1. *Exempli gratia*; 2. Margaret Thatcher; 3. The Red Ensign; 4. Kashmir goat; 5. Caligula's; 6. 26 miles, 385 yards; 7. Elliott Gould; 8. 18; 9. Ely; 10. 6/7th; 11. 32; 12. Mural; 13. Tony Parsons; 14. Bill Clinton; 15. Boris Becker; 16. David Cameron

QUIZ 19

1. Piccolo; 2. The Miracles; 3. Ballet; 4. Amplitude modulation; 5. Beryl; 6. Lord Byron; 7. Michael Foot; 8. Six; 9. Gallifrey; 10. *Tirpitz*; 11. Ermine Street; 12. Pixels; 13. US president Gerald Ford; 14. Maxilla; 15. Pisa; 16. Show jumping

QUIZ 20

1. Oxford; 2. Matchboxes; 3. Nebula; 4. Thomas Edison; 5. Davy Jones' locker; 6. Teheran; 7. Richard Stilgoe; 8. Elizabeth I; 9. Ship's biscuits; 10. World's Strongest Man; 11. Admiral Karl Doenitz; 12. Dr Zhivago; 13. Brazil; 14. New trend; 15. *Sense and Sensibility*; 16. A maquette

QUIZ 21

1. J Edgar Hoover; 2. Zola Budd; 3. *There Will Be Blood*; 4. Mark Twain;

5. Lyndon Johnson; 6. In his sleep; 7. Aviation; 8. *Fame Academy*; 9. Roland Garros; 10. Mt Olympus; 11. 1870; 12. Creedence Clearwater Revival; 13. Wind power; 14. 1947; 15. David Walliams; 16. Romania

QUIZ 22 (Science & Nature)
1. Penguin; 2. The skin; 3. Four; 4. Tungsten; 5. Watercress; 6. Cirrus; 7. Mobile phone; 8. Spinning jenny; 9. CERN; 10. Cob; 11. Monkey; 12. Epsom salts; 13. Rachel Carson; 14. Anti-clockwise; 15. Five billion; 16. Scrape

QUIZ 23
1. Sir Edwin Landseer; 2. Andalucia; 3. China; 4. Princess Anne; 5. Wigan Pier; 6. Sea shell; 7. Roscoe 'Fatty' Arbuckle; 8. W G Grace; 9. *Sunset Boulevard*; 10. There's no difference; 11. Morrissey; 12. Edward Heath; 13. Rotheram; 14. Martial arts weapon; 15. Tim Vincent; 16. Progress through technology

QUIZ 24
1. DCCLXXVII; 2. Lock; 3. Alan Sugar's; 4. Van Dyck (later Sir Anthony Vandyke); 5. Snowy; 6. Mike Gatting; 7. Fanny Craddock; 8. Therefore; 9. Massachusetts; 10. Electric charge; 11. Zurich; 12. Tax evasion; 13. Japanese musical instrument; 14. Werner von Braun; 15. John Peter Rhys; 16. Gavin Troy

QUIZ 25
1. Urdu; 2. *The Count of Monte Cristo*; 3. When the moon is more than half but less than full; 4. Artem Chigvintsev; 5. Bath; 6. Julian Barnes; 7. Munro; 8. Ronald Reagan; 9. 'Green, Green Grass Of Home'; 10. Madrid; 11. George Washington's; 12. Spain and Portugal; 13. Dublin; 14. Dog Star; 15. Casanova; 16. Gyllenhaal

QUIZ 26

1. Robert Plant; 2. Australia; 3. National lottery; 4. St Matthew;
5. Psychology; 6. Robert Maxwell; 7. Grimaldi; 8. Daniel Defoe; 9. 'Can we fix it?'; 10. Francis Pym; 11. Hector Berlioz; 12. Argentine peso;
13. Ravi Shastri; 14. The Netherlands; 15. Oxford Committee for Famine Relief; 16. Arundel

QUIZ 27

1. *Of Thee I Sing*; 2. China and Nepal; 3. David Beckham's; 4. Thou shalt not kill; 5. Virgil; 6. Ringo Starr; 7. Fair wind; 8. Alan Michael Sugar Trading; 9. Upper edge of the hull; 10. *Coquille*; 11. Jeff Beck;
12. Maple White Land; 13. Battle of Jutland; 14. Rabbit; 15. Egypt;
16. François Truffaut

QUIZ 28

1. Eight; 2. *Daniel Deronda*; 3. 22; 4. Esther and Abi Ofarim; 5. Sugar Ray Robinson's; 6. James I; 7. Mercury; 8. Railway; 9. Robert Frost;
10. Salisbury; 11. Yes; 12. Three; 13. Jan Vermeer; 14. Sir Robert Walpole;
15. Supernova; 16. Geena Davis

QUIZ 29

1. Georgia and Alabama; 2. Suspicion; 3. Hercule Poirot; 4. Ox-like;
5. Wings; 6. Richard Wagner; 7. Hieronymus Bosch; 8. Duke of Wellington's; 9. Kermit the frog; 10. On its toes; 11. William Webb Ellis;
12. Fernando Alonso (Ferrari); 13. Lulu; 14. Porsche; 15. Trailer park;
16. Kiwi

QUIZ 30

1. Manchester United; 2. Red; 3. South Dakota; 4. Leicester; 5. Osborne House; 6. Airstrip One; 7. Having a haircut; 8. Paul McCartney; 9. Withers;
10. Camp David; 11. The Pope's; 12. Kolkata; 13. Kenneth Branagh and Emma Thompson; 14. Fast tempo; 15. Procrastination; 16. Skye

QUIZ 31 (Music)

1. Depeche Mode; 2. You Tube; 3. Sharon Osbourne; 4. 'Here I Go Again'; 5. Olivia Newton-John's; 6. 2006; 7. Duke Ellington, Earl Hines, Count Basie; 8. 'Fingal's Cave'; 9. Clint Eastwood; 10. 15; 11. David Baddiel and Frank Skinner; 12. Germany; 13. Madonna; 14. Little Stevie Wonder; 15. Eric Coates; 16. Blue

QUIZ 32

1. Pakistan; 2. C, O and S; 3. Ambergris; 4. Dior; 5. Harriet Beecher Stowe; 6. Jonathan Pryce; 7. Higher; 8. Antarctica; 9. The Scaffold ('Thank You Very Much'); 10. Spinner's End; 11. Al Murray; 12. European Monetary System; 13. 32; 14. Your Grace; 15. Rembrandt; 16. Russia

QUIZ 33

1. Cambodia; 2. Shave; 3. Finland; 4. Hedonist; 5. Badminton; 6. Clive Dunn; 7. Sheep; 8. Old Testament; 9. Because of their tarred pigtails; 10. *Steamboat Willie*; 11. Harold Macmillan; 12. John Donne; 13. The Blind Beggar (Whitechapel); 14. Ringo Starr; 15. Lawyer; 16. Cain and Abel

QUIZ 34

1. Scallions; 2. Sam Wanamaker; 3. Thistle; 4. Gloucestershire; 5. Shergar; 6. Bates Motel; 7. 17; 8. Food; 9. Devonshire; 10. Annie Lennox; 11. Grasmere (Cumbria); 12. 1910; 13. Symphony No 2; 14. Chicago; 15. Lou Reed; 16. Electric battery

QUIZ 35

1. Cape Town; 2. Balaclava; 3. Iain Duncan Smith; 4. 54; 5. Marriage; 6. James Lillywhite; 7. Nose bleed; 8. Frankie Laine; 9. M J K Smith (he won a rugby Test cap); 10. Brendan Behan; 11. Red River; 12. Knight Errant; 13. Emu (three); 14. Imelda Marcos; 15. Brown; 16. Inter-Cities Cup

QUIZ 36

1. 26; 2. Roald Amundsen; 3. Freya's; 4. Turin; 5. Costa Rica; 6. *The Alamo*;
7. Franklin Delano Roosevelt; 8. Atlantic; 9. Goat; 10. Christopher
Marlowe; 11. Mary Wilson; 12. Ants; 13. Cape Wrath; 14. Viv Richards;
15. Tuna and anchovies; 16. George Clooney

QUIZ 37

1. The Statue of Liberty; 2. Mozart; 3. *Play Away*; 4. Christine Lagarde;
5. Élysée Palace; 6. Cerberus; 7. Neva; 8. Princess Anne's; 9. St Clare of
Assisi; 10. Canoeing; 11. Loretta Lynn's; 12. John Entwistle;
13. Switchblade; 14. Ariel Sharon; 15. Unfermented grape juice;
16. Nyasaland

QUIZ 38 (History)

1. Korean War; 2. Adolf Hitler; 3. Ireland; 4. First regular bus service;
5. 1987; 6. Woodrow Wilson; 7. Charles II; 8. Queen Juliana; 9. 1961;
10. Henrik Verwoerd; 11. Amelia Earhart; 12. Ethelred II; 13. Queen Anne;
14. Treaty of Rome; 15. House of Hanover; 16. Alcohol

QUIZ 39

1. Duke and Duchess of York; 2. Red and white; 3. *The Rights of Man*;
4. Plastic; 5. Chaps; 6. Colombia; 7. General Douglas MacArthur
(*MacArthur*); 8. Persia; 9. Diahnne Abbott; 10. April; 11. Silver fern;
12. Lord Longford; 13. Denmark; 14. Maurice Jarre; 15. 1886; 16. Hover

QUIZ 40

1. Ozone; 2. Lana Turner's; 3. Michael Mann; 4. Hungary; 5. Cook Islands;
6. Entente Cordiale; 7. Hungary; 8. Charon; 9. Macavity; 10. 168; 11. The
Artful Dodger; 12. Pig; 13. *The Diary of a Nobody*; 14. Ten; 15. Marilyn
Monroe; 16. Study of glands

QUIZ 41

1. Cantilever; 2. Julia Gillard; 3. Equestrianism; 4. Time and Relative Dimension in Space; 5. Glissando; 6. Venus; 7. Euphegenia; 8. Gary Brooker; 9. Commander of the Order of the British Empire; 10. Granada; 11. Catalan; 12. Cardinal Richelieu; 13. Cow (*vacca*); 14. Anne Robinson; 15. Harold Macmillan; 16. Spice Girls

QUIZ 42

1. New Mexico; 2. Margaret Thatcher; 3. Dr Emmett Brown (*Back to the Future*); 4. Seven; 5. Kathryn Howard; 6. Bun; 7. Po; 8. Club foot; 9. Irwin Shaw; 10. H M Stanley; 11. Johannes Brahms; 12. Lord Baden-Powell; 13. Snakewood; 14. 1904; 15. Oxford English Dictionary; 16. Mississippi

QUIZ 43

1. Chess; 2. Monaco; 3. Arthur Conan Doyle; 4. Stamen; 5. *The Old Devils*; 6. Michael Parkinson; 7. Bauxite; 8. Bruce Springsteen; 9. Marcia Falkender; 10. Goulash; 11. Australia; 12. Henry; 13. Seven-spotted ladybird; 14. Mark Thatcher; 15. Mary-Kate Olsen; 16. Barry Gibb

QUIZ 44

1. Wessex; 2. France; 3. Steel; 4. Ear; 5. 18th; 6. Myanmar (Burma); 7. Aneurin Bevan; 8. Beards; 9. Cosa Nostra; 10. Leander; 11. Katherine Hepburn; 12. 828m (2716ft); 13. Blackcurrant; 14. Sandro Botticelli; 15. Postcards; 16. Kenny Everett's

QUIZ 45 (Geography)

1. New South Wales; 2. Azerbaijan; 3. Cuba; 4. Red Square (Moscow); 5. Italy and Switzerland; 6. The Roaring Forties; 7. Sudan; 8. Dover; 9. Negev; 10. French (dialect); 11. Vietnam; 12. Montréal-Trudeau (Pierre Trudeau); 13. Danzig; 14. Sargasso; 15. Durham; 16. Murmansk

QUIZ 46

1. Bob Geldof and Midge Ure; 2. Four; 3. Eddie Waring's; 4. Kangaroo; 5. Britain and Spain; 6. Left; 7. Henry James; 8. Céline Dion; 9. Portugal; 10. Great work; 11. Sleuth; 12. Brig; 13. Gliding; 14. Stephen Maturin; 15. Hamlet's father; 16. Queensland and Northern Territory Aerial Service

QUIZ 47

1. Aled Jones; 2. Canadian; 3. Capsicin; 4. Norah Jones; 5. American Civil War; 6. Drew Barrymore; 7. Sir Arthur Sullivan; 8. Dominique Strauss-Kahn; 9. Edinburgh Castle; 10. Bedrock; 11. Bicycle motocross; 12. *Scissor Sisters*; 13. Paul; 14. Ezra Pound; 15. Dr Robert Runcie; 16. Gang

QUIZ 48

1. Siegfried Sassoon ; 2. Femur (thigh bone); 3. USA (110); 4. Barbara Marx; 5. Karl Marx; 6. Michael Jackson; 7. Organisation of Petroleum Exporting Countries; 8. Two; 9. James Bolam and Susan Jameson; 10. Pig-like mammal; 11. John Buchan; 12. William Frederick Cody; 13. Norwich; 14. 100 billion; 15. Pablo Picasso; 16. Durham

QUIZ 49

1. Electrocardiogram; 2. Portugal; 3. Wat Tyler; 4. No; 5. Martha Washington; 6. Central; 7. Tasmania; 8. French bean; 9. Filly; 10. Kay Kendall; 11. Felix; 12. Cricket; 13. Clyde McPhatter; 14. Sappho; 15. Bailey; 16. Bumfreezer

QUIZ 50

1. Piraeus; 2. Simón Bolivar; 3. Tom Jones; 4. Nymph; 5. *Prix Goncourt*; 6. 28; 7. Royal Institute of British Architects; 8. Alan Johnston; 9. Russia; 10. Loire; 11. Aretha Franklin; 12. Thomas Pynchon; 13. Die; 14. Dave Brubeck; 15. Alec Issigonis; 16. 7920

QUIZ 51

1. Tchaikovsky; 2. Panama hat; 3. Beetle; 4. Au; 5. Lena Zavaroni;
6. St Louis; 7. Jacob Marley; 8. Ten; 9. H; 10. Five; 11. Friedrich Schiller's;
12. Liverpool; 13. Baltimore; 14. John Carpenter; 15. St Christopher;
16. Swagman's bundle

QUIZ 52 (Sport)

1. India; 2. 14; 3. Russia; 4. 46g; 5. Beards; 6. Driver error; 7. Fanny
Blankers-Koen; 8. Winners of the NFL Super Bowl (USA); 9. Martin Offiah;
10. Christopher Martin-Jenkins; 11. Gordon Strachan; 12. Corey Pavin;
13. Pink; 14. Seven; 15. Brazilian; 16. The Bourda Oval, Georgetown

QUIZ 53

1. Andrew Ridgeley; 2. Image; 3. Crescent and star; 4. Velvet; 5. Scott
Joplin's; 6. *Prima facie*; 7. Speedway racing; 8. Westminster Abbey;
9. Pelham Grenville; 10. Anthony Blunt; 11. Adelaide; 12. Donald Duck's
nephews; 13. 1903; 14. Ashton Kutcher; 15. Iceland; 16. The Althing

QUIZ 54

1. Wednesday; 2. Henry Mancini; 3. 1988; 4. Taipei; 5. George Marshall
(The Marshall Plan); 6. Pottery; 7. Duke of Gloucester; 8. It means both;
9. Shakespeare's; 10. Pedro Almodóvar; 11. Louis Theroux; 12. Malcolm
X; 13. The tank ('The Land Ironclads'); 14. Katherine Jenkins and Darcey
Bussell; 15. Mandolin; 16. A hat

QUIZ 55

1. Quasi-Autonomous Non-Governmental Organisation; 2. Howitzer;
3. John Wilkes Booth; 4. Bruce Forsyth-Johnson; 5. Maine; 6. The Police;
7. 1992; 8. Pak-choi; 9. White Sea; 10. Aden; 11. Carlos the Jackal;
12. Fairy tales; 13. Peter Parker; 14. N; 15. Jules; 16. Verwoerdburg

QUIZ 56

1. Amadeus; 2. Malta, Gozo, Comino; 3. Reverend Wilbert Awdry;
4. Standard Oil (enunciation of initials); 5. André Previn; 6. *Crazy Heart*;
7. Hermes; 8. History; 9. Helen Sharman; 10. Vic Reeves; 11. Northern;
12. Henry Miller's; 13. 1922; 14. Jamie Cullum's; 15. Eight; 16. Fatted
goose liver

QUIZ 57

1. Harry Truman; 2. Nicholas Blake; 3. Strang; 4. Richard Nixon;
5. St George's Channel; 6. Webb Ellis Cup; 7. Endeavour; 8. *Prisoner of
Azkaban*; 9. Belshazzar; 10. Roger Moore's; 11. 1972; 12. Cucumber;
13. *Blithe Spirit*; 14. Imitation gold; 15. Yew; 16. One-sixth

QUIZ 58

1. Two; 2. Cheese; 3. Mahalia Jackson; 4. Madras; 5. Beyoncé;
6. Austrian; 7. North Carolina; 8. Australia; 9. John Ridd; 10. Elephant;
11. George Brown; 12. Arms; 13. Richard II; 14. Avocado; 15. Three;
16. Algeria

QUIZ 59 (Cinema & TV)

1. *Never Say Never Again*; 2. Advertising; 3. Marty McFly; 4. Nigella
Lawson; 5. Stewart Granger; 6. Dublin; 7. Control; 8. Hollywood Foreign
Press Association; 9. Billy the Kid; 10. Treasurer of Atlantic County;
11. The Pigeon Sisters; 12. Jim Carter; 13. Nick Frost; 14. Chico; 15. Elliott
Bay Towers; 16. Dorothy Michaels

QUIZ 60

1. Vinci; 2. Coconut; 3. Warm; 4. Dolce (Sicilian) and Gabbana (Venetian);
5. Saul; 6. Frances Tomelty; 7. Nigel Pargetter; 8. Fabergé; 9. Nine;
10. Trowbridge; 11. National Association of Securities Dealers
Automatic Quotation; 12. Michelangelo; 13. Miller; 14. River Thames;
15. Sydney Harbour Bridge; 16. Kool & the Gang

QUIZ 61

1. Mrs Hudson; 2. Stanley Baldwin; 3. Peter Toole; 4. Five; 5. Alluvium; 6. Salmon; 7. Mothballs; 8. John Adams; 9. Dog (called Laika); 10. George Lucas; 11. Henry Charles Albert David Wales; 12. Yeast; 13. Kansas; 14. Tooth decay; 15. Isle of Man; 16. Tunisia

QUIZ 62

1. National Aeronautics and Space Administration; 2. Queen Anne; 3. Truro; 4. Sorbonne; 5. Shand; 6. Underground; 7. Dutch East Indies; 8. 28; 9. +34; 10. Vibraphone; 11. David Ben-Gurion; 12. Gustave Mahler's; 13. Commonwealth Star; 14. Venus Flytrap; 15. Lady Godiva; 16. Best Original Song (from *Lord Of The Rings*)

QUIZ 63

1. Elvis Costello; 2. Jack Ruby; 3. France; 4. Nicole Kidman; 5. Study of trees; 6. Michael Colin Cowdrey's; 7. Northern Territory; 8. Poppy; 9. Colin Powell; 10. John Christie; 11. James Joyce; 12. Isle of Man's; 13. Danish; 14. Seahorse; 15. None; 16. Fred West

QUIZ 64

1. Anthony Minghella; 2. P G Wodehouse's; 3. Jacques Chirac; 4. Scilly Isles; 5. New Zealand; 6. Albemarle Street; 7. 1940s; 8. Father; 9. 37; 10. Double-glazing salesman; 11. South China Sea; 12. Claire Rayner; 13. Miniatures; 14. Yahoo; 15. Blackcurrant; 16. 366

QUIZ 65

1. Archduke Franz Ferdinand's; 2. San Andreas; 3. *For Whom the Bell Tolls*; 4. Pope Benedict XVI; 5. *The Oldie*; 6. Black Sea; 7. *Fritto misto*; 8. 'Long Live Love'; 9. Archbishop Cosmo Lang; 10. Yangtze; 11. The Louvre (Paris); 12. He was shot; 13. Harold Macmillan; 14. Oliver Goldsmith; 15. Václav Havel (Czechoslovakia); 16. Newton Heath

QUIZ 66

1. WRAF; 2. Falmouth; 3. Sana'a; 4. Duke of Wellington; 5. Five;
6. University of London; 7. Barbara Cartland's; 8. Pegasus; 9. St Mungo;
10. Winnie Mandela; 11. Ozzy Osbourne; 12. Graham Thorpe;
13. Babylon; 14. Johnny Dankworth; 15. Agra; 16. Lee

QUIZ 67 (Science & Nature)

1. Radon; 2. Carbon dioxide; 3. K; 4. Polar; 5. Brazilian Wandering Spider;
6. Resin; 7. Arm; 8. Iron; 9. Koala; 10. Three; 11. Isaac Newton;
12. Continental shelf; 13. Acquired Immune Deficiency Syndrome;
14. Fox; 15. Hummingbird; 16. Richard Dawkins

QUIZ 68

1. Ira Gershwin; 2. Princess Michael of Kent; 3. Orkneys; 4. Dnieper;
5. Chequers; 6. Kodak; 7. Polish; 8. Bridget Riley; 9. Great-granddaughter;
10. Sign language; 11. Doncaster; 12. Wings; 13. Jimmy Cliff; 14. James
Callaghan; 15. Zechariah; 16. Maracas

QUIZ 69

1. M8; 2. Karl Malden; 3. Shrewsbury; 4. Lord Melbourne; 5. Deringer
pistol; 6. Ireland; 7. Bengali; 8. Abel Magwitch; 9. Pathé; 10. Edward VII;
11. Abigail; 12. Malcolm Maclaren; 13. Mob; 14. Gemini; 15. Wiping off
cold cream; 16. Hull

QUIZ 70

1. J B Priestley; 2. Joe Biden; 3. Magdalane; 4. Kenneth MacDonald;
5. *Velours* (velvet) and *crochet* (hook); 6. Adam and the Ants;
7. Astronaut Alan Shepard (1971); 8. Polyvinyl chloride; 9. Yves Montand;
10. *Iliad*; 11. White lines to mark the middle of the road; 12. Exeter;
13. Standard Oil; 14. Charles II's; 15. Antwerp; 16. 'Tin Lizzie'

QUIZ 71

1. Pat; 2. Study of word origins; 3. Yom Kippur; 4. Audie Murphy; 5. Baseball; 6. *London Evening Standard*; 7. Seven; 8. Horrid Henry; 9. Pink; 10. Charles Mackintosh; 11. Zero Mostel; 12. Japan; 13. Dashiell Hammett; 14. Medusa; 15. Union of Soviet Socialist Republics; 16. Watney's

QUIZ 72

1. Hilary Mantel; 2. The Hee Bee Gee Bees; 3. Horse; 4. *Wisden Cricketers' Almanack*; 5. Jimmy Carter's; 6. Sir Ranulph Fiennes; 7. Michael and John; 8. Titian; 9. It's short for engine; 10. Drunk; 11. Hundredweight; 12. The Righteous Brothers; 13. Australia's national football team; 14. *The Independent*; 15. Keith; 16. Phineas T Barnum

QUIZ 73

1. Brylcreem's; 2. *Ecce Cor Meum* (Behold My Heart); 3. Greenwich Palace; 4. Paper; 5. BBC2; 6. Robin Cook; 7. Eiffel; 8. Chester City (it is partly in Wales, partly in England); 9. Ear; 10. Verona; 11. *The Rocky Horror Picture Show*; 12. England; 13. Anthony Powell's; 14. *Le Figaro*; 15. Scafell Pike; 16. 12

QUIZ 74 (Music)

1. 'It's My Life'; 2. Mýa Marie Harrison; 3. Kelly Clarkson; 4. The Mars Bars; 5. Contralto; 6. 'Relax'; 7. Radio Caroline; 8. 1977; 9. 'The Colonel Bogey March'; 10. Arthur Sullivan; 11. 25; 12. Nicole Scherzinger; 13. Daniel Barenboim; 14. George Michael; 15. 1970; 16. *The Tales of Hoffmann*

QUIZ 75

1. Zadie Smith; 2. Portugal; 3. Edwina Currie; 4. Tin; 5. Sound Navigation and Ranging; 6. David; 7. Greece; 8. Francis; 9. Zither; 10. Four; 11. The Gambia; 12. Great soul; 13. Shingles; 14. Doctor; 15. Sir Ian McGeechan; 16. Kielder Water

QUIZ 76

1. William IV; 2. Rachmaninov's Piano Concerto No 2; 3. Winchester; 4. Christopher Marlowe; 5. Cambodia's; 6. Les Invalides; 7. Fish; 8. John Major (first Gulf War); 9. Vancouver; 10. An alarm clock; 11. Quite interesting; 12. Sir Henry Irving; 13. Flora Thompson; 14. Charles Atlas; 15. St Augustine; 16. Condoleezza Rice

QUIZ 77

1. England; 2. Samuel Pepys; 3. New Guinea; 4. Lurcio; 5. British Commonwealth; 6. Newcastle; 7. John Churchill; 8. 1965; 9. 336; 10. Ayers Rock; 11. 15 September; 12. Rook; 13. Bilbo Baggins; 14. Fay Weldon's; 15. The Nag's Head; 16. An intrusion

QUIZ 78

1. Rabat; 2. David Simon; 3. Oak; 4. Pat Garrett; 5. Bee; 6. *The Hitchhiker's Guide to the Galaxy*; 7. Malachi; 8. *Mercredi*; 9. Dutch; 10. Great Dune of Pyla (France); 11. Hundred Acre Wood; 12. 27; 13. Battle of Kursk; 14. 16th; 15. Nautical mile; 16. *Gulliver's Travels*

QUIZ 79

1. George Best; 2. Amsterdam; 3. Vincent Van Gogh's; 4. DCI Gene Hunt; 5. Jay Rayner; 6. Dick Cheney; 7. Lawnmower; 8. Hypertext Mark-up Language; 9. Entomology; 10. Tasman Sea; 11. Gareth Jenkins; 12. Jennifer Hudson; 13. John Sullivan; 14. J M W Turner; 15. James Stewart; 16. Calf

QUIZ 80

1. England and Scotland (1872); 2. Boycie and Marlene (*The Green Green Grass*); 3. Vitamin D; 4. Alexander Pope; 5. Fully dehydrated; 6. J D Salinger; 7. Wahlberg; 8. David Mellor; 9. Siberian Tiger; 10. Newport (IOW); 11. Wormwood Scrubs; 12. Wrist; 13. Pomelo; 14. Lewis Carroll; 15. Ravi Bopara; 16. Women

QUIZ 81

1. Anthony Trollope; 2. Basketball; 3. Egypt; 4. *Daily Planet*; 5. Two;
6. Jerez; 7. Charles Darwin; 8. Princess Eugenie; 9. China; 10. Bann;
11. State Registered Nurse; 12. Kofi Anna; 13. Madagascar; 14. Boom;
15. 24; 16. World altitude record

QUIZ 82 (History)

1. Battle of Little Big Horn; 2. Herbert Asquith; 3. Abraham Lincoln;
4. Rajiv Gandhi; 5. 33 days; 6. Wolf's Lair; 7. George VI; 8. Leon Trotsky;
9. Hare; 10. Queen Victoria's; 11. Mary Queen of Scots; 12. Australia;
13. General George S Patton; 14. Alexander the Great; 15. Michael
Dukakis; 16. Edward II

QUIZ 83

1. Caerphilly Castle; 2. Deadly Nightshade; 3. Three; 4. Love letter;
5. Corfu; 6. Belgium, France, Germany; 7. Tennessee Williams; 8. Morris
Garages; 9. St Crispin's; 10. Three; 11. Long winded; 12. Webbed; 13. Six;
14. Alexander Graham Bell; 15. Luanda; 16. Isambard Kingdom Brunel

QUIZ 84

1. Alec Stewart; 2. Shopping centres; 3. Bailey; 4. Her breast; 5. Nancy
Pelosi; 6. Wood; 7. Tony Williams; 8. Won; 9. Croydon; 10. Son-in-law;
11. Typhus; 12. Padua; 13. Scottish crown jewels; 14. Five; 15. Swamp;
16. *The Imaginarium of Doctor Parnassus*

QUIZ 85

1. Dover Castle; 2. 1 November; 3. Laurence Olivier; 4. Oxford; 5. *Albert
Herring*, by Benjamin Britten; 6. Gibraltar; 7. Terry Lloyd; 8. Sir Peter Hall;
9. Kiki Dee; 10. Minnesota Mining and Manufacturing; 11. Pele;
12. Benjamin Disraeli; 13. Dutch; 14. Ben Warris; 15. Salisbury;
16. Captain Flint

QUIZ 86

1. Russell Brand; 2. Branwell Brontë; 3. United Arab Emirates; 4. Rimsky-Korsakov; 5. West Germany; 6. Oxford; 7. Radio Luxembourg;
8. Sir Wilfred Thesiger; 9. James; 10. Gold; 11. Kuala Lumpur (Petronas Towers); 12. Reinforced steel joist; 13. Four; 14. David; 15. Sunflower;
16. Fan

QUIZ 87

1. St Andrew's; 2. Anwar Sadat; 3. Tigris; 4. 15 July; 5. Rick Stein;
6. Algae; 7. Art forgery; 8. Robotic; 9. John Denver; 10. Jomo Kenyatta;
11. Oxford and Cambridge; 12. Rafter; 13. Ebony; 14. Ruth Ellis; 15. King cobra; 16. Frank Sinatra

QUIZ 88

1. Egpyt; 2. Lord Warden of the Cinque Ports; 3. Phil Spector; 4. France;
5. Neptune; 6. William H Bonney; 7. Bordeaux; 8. Chris Patten; 9. Farrow;
10. Approx. 1.25cm (1/2in); 11. Captain Nemo; 12. Florence;
13. William Whitelaw; 14. Mika Hakkinen; 15. Juggernaut; 16. Stanley Matthews

QUIZ 89 (Geography)

1. Dartmoor; 2. Isle of Wight; 3. Canada; 4. Auckland; 5. Alaska;
6. Romania; 7. Montevideo; 8. Hudson; 9. Everglades; 10. River Ouse;
11. Fremantle Doctor; 12. Lundy Island; 13. Arctic; 14. Chelmsford;
15. Mali; 16. Paraguay's

QUIZ 90

1. Sidney Lumet; 2. Charles Reade; 3. White blood cells; 4. Boys Brigade;
5. Guernica; 6. Vanillin; 7. Edith Piaf; 8. Taxi drivers; 9. The Flowerpot Men; 10. Daddy Longlegs; 11. Lacrosse; 12. Sidney Nolan; 13. Melanie Chisholm; 14. Rodent; 15. Benny Goodman; 16. Alan Freeman's

QUIZ 91

1. Lang Lang; 2. War of American Independence; 3. 1615; 4. 500; 5. Lord (Chris) Patten; 6. Hydrogen; 7. *The Simpsons*; 8. John Donne; 9. Waldorf; 10. Pendulum 11. Oxford United; 12. Copper and tin; 13. Mike Newall; 14. 1938; 15. *The Sunday Times*; 16. Portugal

QUIZ 92

1. 1995; 2. Four; 3. 'Hope that helps'; 4. Battle of Midway; 5. Mark Hughes; 6. Large Hadron Collider; 7. Sir Robin Day; 8. Flute; 9. Four; 10. Fortinbras; 11. India; 12. 'I Should Be So Lucky'; 13. Advisory Conciliation and Arbitration Service; 14. Credit card fraud; 15. Kilometre; 16. William Frith

QUIZ 93

1. Wikipedia; 2. Severn; 3. English Civil War; 4. ETA; 5. *Bleak House*; 6. Marie Stopes; 7. Bee hummingbird; 8. Isar; 9. Lodge; 10. Spruce Goose; 11. François Pienaar; 12. Watts; 13. Keith Moon; 14. 13; 15. Nettles; 16. West Germany

QUIZ 94

1. Jack Cohen; 2. 2002; 3. Sir Simon Rattle; 4. 20; 5. Netherlands; 6. Battle royal; 7. *Minder*; 8. Kookaburra; 9. Vertical; 10. Edward Morgan; 11. Seven (*Seven Pillars of Wisdom*); 12. Vera Brittain; 13. Robert Stroud; 14. Small secluded valley; 15. 2, 3, 5 and 7; 16. River Phoenix

QUIZ 95

1. Napoleon; 2. Sir George Young; 3. Pincus; 4. Jackson Pollock; 5. Loch Lomond; 6. Faggot; 7. James I's; 8. The world's first skyscraper; 9. Home Insurance Building, Chicago; 10. George Harrison; 11. Parrot; 12. Water; 13. Fine by eleven; 14. Bristol; 15. Conversation; 16. Norman Foster

QUIZ 96 (Sport)

1. Surrey Lions; 2. South Africa and Wales; 3. Hockey; 4. West Germany;
5. Begin; 6. Squash; 7. That a faster car is trying to overtake; 8. Roche;
9. Faster, Higher, Stronger; 10. Sir Alec Douglas-Home; 11. Evander
Holyfield's; 12. 1¼ miles (2km); 13. Eric Liddell; 14. Martin Keown;
15. Bellerive Oval; 16. 400m freestyle

QUIZ 97

1. Before the flood; 2. *Elf*; 3. Jack Dawkins; 4. The Urals; 5. First Lord of
the Admiralty; 6. Wystan Hugh; 7. Skiing; 8. Charlotte Church;
9. Trousers; 10. *Call For the Dead*; 11. North; 12. Mir orbital station;
13. Polonius; 14. John Harvey-Jones; 15. Nevada; 16. Jack Lemmon

QUIZ 98

1. The letter E; 2. France; 3. 1986; 4. Mr Bean; 5. Black pool;
6. Hairdressing; 7. Cable News Network; 8. Australia Capital Territory;
9. Carthage; 10. 'The Medal of Honor'; 11. Northampton Town;
12. Paul McCartney and Ringo Starr; 13. Ngaio Marsh; 14. Henry VI;
15. Dragonfly; 16. Sound

QUIZ 99

1. Yarmulke; 2. Male donkey and female horse; 3. Fratricide; 4. Dover;
5. Madame Butterfly; 6. Moisture in the atmosphere; 7. Primates;
8. Club foot; 9. 'I'm Always Chasing Rainbows'; 10. Harper Seven;
11. Diving; 12. Victoria line; 13. Jack Rosenthal; 14. 'The Combine
Harvester'; 15. 50; 16. Lagoon

QUIZ 100

1. Whitewash; 2. Ava Gardner; 3. Avocado; 4. Raki; 5. Michael Caine;
6. Russian; 7. Burial mound; 8. Saint-Nazaire, France; 9. Manchester;
10. The Moody Blues; 11. Seven; 12. Sean O'Casey; 13. Magma; 14. King
Solomon; 15. George Mortimer Pullman; 16. Islay

QUIZ 101

1. Paul; 2. Brimstone; 3. Edith Cresson; 4. Radioactivity; 5. Argentina;
6. John; 7. Chris Lewis; 8. Smoking; 9. Tomato; 10. Topiary; 11. Nelson
Mandela's; 12. The Animals; 13. Hair; 14. Twilight of the Gods;
15. George Bernard Shaw; 16. Gun (cannon)

QUIZ 102

1. Australia; 2. Dried meat; 3. Javier Bardem; 4. Beetle; 5. Mediterranean;
6. Cat Stevens; 7. Golden Lion; 8. York; 9. Richard II; 10. Zambezi;
11. Prince Philip (1961); 12. Campanology; 13. Bottom of sea or lake;
14. Walker; 15. Q and Z; 16. Spring

QUIZ 103

1. Conrad Murray; 2. Delhi; 3. David Dickinson; 4. *Moby Dick*; 5. Peter
Scott; 6. 2ft (0.6m); 7. Ayr; 8. Rod Stewart; 9. Burundi; 10. Delft; 11. René
Descartes; 12. Divine wind; 13. Gregorian; 14. Comma; 15. Milkman;
16. Aaron Copland

QUIZ 104 (Cinema & TV)

1. *The Italian Job*; 2. Emma Watson; 3. Harry Enfield's; 4. Clown Fish;
5. HMP Slade; 6. *Julia*; 7. *All in the Family*; 8. Pinkie Brown; 9. Alan Alda's;
10. Celia Imrie; 11. *Silverado*; 12. Hugh Fraser; 13. *Cairo*; 14. Kurt
Wallander; 15. *It's Always Fair Weather*; 16. Blofeld (in James Bond films)

QUIZ 105

1. Jools Holland's; 2. Pickles; 3. J M Coetzee; 4. 1972; 5. Dien Bien Phu;
6. Beau; 7. Burt Bacharach and Hal David; 8. Green, white, red;
9. Conquest, War, Famine, Death; 10. A tittering; 11. 1960;
12. Rudolf Hess; 13. Charles Lindburgh; 14. Four; 15. Borneo; 16. 'John
Kettley (Is A Weatherman)'

QUIZ 106

1. 'We Are Family'; 2. Think tank (on international affairs); 3. Bikini;
4. Pancreas; 5. Benjamin Franklin; 6. James Graham; 7. Balsa; 8. Sicily;
9. Iran-Iraq; 10. Charles Foster Kane's in *Citizen Kane*; 11. Bad Homburg
(homburg hat); 12. Kukri; 13. Vincent Van Gogh; 14. Weights and
measures; 15. Lord Lucan; 16. Peter Sellers and Sophia Loren

QUIZ 107

1. Stephen; 2. Bird; 3. *Bleak House*; 4. Both have 24; 5. Irish Moss; 6. Lord
Castlereagh; 7. Fibre-optic Link Around the Globe; 8. Sparky; 9. His sense
of smell; 10. Dylan Thomas; 11. 'You Can Leave Your Hat On'; 12. 3m;
13. Lizzie Borden; 14. Switzerland; 15. Ryan Giggs; 16. Hawaii

QUIZ 108

1. George IV; 2. 'Eleven pipers piping'; 3. Animals without backbones;
4. John Haigh; 5. The Lord's Taverners; 6. Peru; 7. Treaty of Versailles;
8. Banknotes; 9. Eton College; 10. Apple; 11. W J Burley; 12. Piracy;
13. 'Dream A Little Dream Of Me'; 14. 18, 18 on the pitch, 4 off;
15. Royal Flying Corps; 16. Malcolm X

QUIZ 109

1. Golf; 2. Blubber; 3. Kate Winslet; 4. Thomas Edward; 5. Alan Price;
6. Boer leader Paul Kruger; 7. France's; 8. Four; 9. County Antrim;
10. British; 11. York; 12. Tennessee; 13. Georgia; 14. Grizabella; 15. Four;
16. Grapeshot

QUIZ 110

1. Canada; 2. Henri Charrière's (*Papillon*); 3. Louis XIV; 4. Ypres; 5. *High
Society*; 6. Bolero; 7. Compton Mackenzie; 8. Obituaries; 9. Navy, Army
and Air Force Institutes; 10. Ennio Morricone; 11. Monty Panesar;
12. Mulberry leaves; 13. Baldwin; 14. Henry Kissinger; 15. Potato;
16. Ponte Vecchio

QUIZ 111 (Science & Nature)

1. Swiss; 2. Vitamin C; 3. Portable Document File; 4. Quicklime; 5. Finch; 6. Windpipe; 7. Hippocrates; 8. 16; 9. Crash; 10. The sea; 11. Five; 12. Thunderfly; 13. Carbon; 14. Boiling; 15. Heat of chilli peppers; 16. Binary

QUIZ 112

1. Cold; 2. Justin Bieber; 3. Ceylon (Sirimavo Bandaranaike); 4. Benjamin Britten; 5. Backgammon; 6. John Updike; 7. Giuseppe Farina (1950); 8. Giza; 9. Dorchester; 10. Eight; 11. William Shakespeare; 12. Dickie Valentine; 13. Eleanor Roosevelt; 14. West Ham; 15. Edward III; 16. Yellowstone

QUIZ 113

1. Eli Whitney; 2. Monza; 3. Winston Smith; 4. Supreme Headquarters Allied Powers in Europe; 5. Spencer Tracy; 6. Omega; 7. Francis Albert; 8. William Caxton; 9. Roy Hattersley; 10. Prince; 11. Clarence Birdseye; 12. Herm; 13. Lance Klusener; 14. Knesset; 15. St Pancras station; 16. Airey Neave

QUIZ 114

1. Niece; 2. Dreadlocks; 3. George Best's; 4. Alison Krauss; 5. Trampolining; 6. *The Hunchback of Notre Dame*; 7. Munich; 8. La Bourse; 9. None; 10. Midas; 11. Anthony Shaffer; 12. 1979; 13. Mr (Michael) Fish; 14. Temperature; 15. Snooker (Ronnie O'Sullivan); 16. Arizona

QUIZ 115

1. Tonto (in *The Lone Ranger*); 2. Skegness; 3. Chair; 4. Samantha Womack; 5. Butterfly; 6. Athens and Sparta; 7. Eldrick Tont; 8. Thomas De Quincey; 9. Silver; 10. Willie John McBride; 11. 2nd February; 12. Dorothy Parker; 13. Raising and draining water; 14. King Farouk; 15. Nipper; 16. Lauren Cooper

QUIZ 116

1. Dab; 2. The Orange Award; 3. Charlemagne; 4. Tit; 5. *World At One*;
6. Washington Irving; 7. Greenland; 8. Michael Holding; 9. Right;
10. Serge Gainsbourg and Jane Birkin; 11. Curling; 12. Glyndebourne;
13. Sean McLoughlin; 14. Jet engines; 15. Bing Crosby; 16. Bahrain

QUIZ 117

1. RAF's; 2. 'Through adversity to the stars'; 3. Norman Stanley Fletcher;
4. June Carter Cash; 5. Tor; 6. Fashanu; 7. Laird; 8. The Lord Chamberlain's
Men; 9. Lancelot 'Capability' Brown; 10. Elton John; 11. Fish;
12. Macadam road surface; 13. Fishing flies; 14. Twice cooked;
15. Auxiliary Territorial Service; 16. Geoffrey Rush

QUIZ 118

1. William IV; 2. General Synod; 3. Dennis Skinner MP; 4. *Chambres
d'hôtes*; 5. Bill Morris; 6. T S Eliot's; 7. General Galtieri; 8. Castle;
9. Jordan and Peter Andre; 10. The sun; 11. The Dam Busters;
12. Newmarket; 13. Richard Madeley's; 14. Lester Piggott; 15. Bill
Clinton; 16. Shetland Islands

QUIZ 119 (Music)

1. Pet Shop Boys; 2. Chris Barber's; 3. Travis; 4. Chris Blackwell; 5. Shorty
Long's; 6. Dario Marianelli's; 7. Thom Yorke; 8. 'Light My Fire'; 9. Paul
McCartney; 10. 'Everybody Hurts'; 11. British Gas; 12. Damita Jo;
13. Randy Sparks; 14. Leonard Bernstein; 15. Chaka Khan; 16. Jennifer
Eccles'

QUIZ 120

1. South Africa; 2. The Doge; 3. Dripping; 4. Grass; 5. Pacemaker;
6. David Taylor; 7. Memory data storage device; 8. Wanda in *A Fish Called
Wanda*; 9. 'Got To Be There'; 10. Wilfred Owen; 11. 1972; 12. British
United Provident Association; 13. John Constable; 14. George III;
15. George Cross; 16. Ken Bates

QUIZ 121

1. Barbados; 2. Floating plant; 3. North Yorkshire; 4. Rocinante;
5. Warsaw; 6. Christmas Day (1995); 7. I came, I saw, I conquered;
8. Florida; 9. Karl Marx; 10. David Helfgott; 11. Carved naked giant;
12. John Huston; 13. Star of David; 14. Wyoming, Montana, Idaho;
15. Harlem Globetrotters; 16. £2 coin

QUIZ 122

1. Swan; 2. Type For You; 3. Stella Remington; 4. 15; 5. Distance;
6. William Beveridge's; 7. Michael Crichton; 8. Michael Douglas;
9. Execution; 10. Greyfriars; 11. Uranus; 12. *Albion Market*; 13. 11;
14. 1941; 15. Silver Ghost; 16. Bulgaria

QUIZ 123

1. Radio Corporation of America; 2. Forge; 3. The Rose Theatre;
4. St Helier; 5. Esso; 6. Swiss franc; 7. *The Blue Lamp* (became *Dixon of Dock Green*); 8. Gladys Pugh; 9. Christopher Booker; 10. Typhoid;
11. Harry Carpenter's; 12. *Henry V*; 13. John Bercow; 14. Hale-Bopp;
15. E; 16. Biba

QUIZ 124

1. V-shaped; 2. Hubert Humphrey; 3. Baseball; 4. Tarsus; 5. Grover
Cleveland; 6. *Requiem in D Minor*; 7. Rank and file of the 1914 British
Expeditionary Force; 8. Andes; 9. Lady Isobel Barnett; 10. Rabbit;
11. Tom Ewell; 12. Baked beans; 13. Glamorgan; 14. Epsilon;
15. Alexander Pope; 16. Third cousin once removed

QUIZ 125

1. Ronald Reagan's; 2. Slipper; 3. Kipper; 4. Kiribati; 5. 1990; 6. Nine;
7. Polymath; 8. Anthony Eden; 9. Water polo; 10. Lake Havasu City,
Arizona; 11. Nitrogen; 12. Edward VII's; 13. *Twelfth Night*; 14. Puffin;
15. Paul Gascoigne; 16. Black, red, yellow

QUIZ 126 (History)

1. 1975; 2. Admiral Sir John Jellicoe; 3. Sharpeville Massacre; 4. Paul von Hindenburg; 5. William I (1066); 6. 24; 7. Prisons; 8. Tito; 9. Teddy Roosevelt; 10. Yom Kippur War; 11. Umberto II; 12. Napoleon and Wellington; 13. Jacobin Club; 14. Judge Jeffreys; 15. Melbourne; 16. Augustus Caesar

QUIZ 127

1. *Northanger Abbey*; 2. Fishing rights; 3. Spurs; 4. Big toe; 5. Winchester; 6. 1952; 7. Gok Wan; 8. Obtuse; 9. Federico García Lorca; 10. Ash Wednesday; 11. Crow's Nest; 12. Photography; 13. BBC radio channels; 14. Mongooses; 15. Queen of the Fairies; 16. Ayr

QUIZ 128

1. *Today*; 2. Bluebell; 3. Mouth organ; 4. 1974; 5. Brandon De Wilde; 6. Leave as is; 7. Best; 8. Klapka; 9. Bobby Fischer; 10. Iron Age; 11. Helen Mirren; 12. Belgian; 13. Board; 14. Meteoric fireball; 15. Former school; 16. Dame Edna Everage

QUIZ 129

1. Bryan Robson's; 2. Jim Broadbent; 3. Intensity of an earthquake; 4. Eros; 5. *The Tempest*; 6. *Herald of Free Enterprise*; 7. 1978-9; 8. Sir Walter Scott's; 9. Paris; 10. The indentation between nose and upper lip; 11. Two (London and Westminster); 12. Israel; 13. Five; 14. Pith helmet (from the plant's dried pith); 15. Pinking shears; 16. Macy Gray

QUIZ 130

1. Third empire; 2. Two; 3. Pear; 4. Neptune; 5. Red, green, blue; 6. Mark Wallinger's; 7. David Bowie; 8. Liz Hurley; 9. Strange or foreign; 10. Boreas; 11. Cousin; 12. Dr Samuel Johnson; 13. Markka; 14. Rome (1960); 15. Dauphin; 16. Paul Scott

QUIZ 131

1. Woody Allen; 2. Cormac McCarthy; 3. Argos; 4. Fungus; 5. 19; 6. Trombone; 7. 'Swear It Again'; 8. Woburn Abbey; 9. Campbells slew the MacDonalds; 10. Passion Play; 11. Ganesa; 12. Abebe Bikila; 13. James Earl Ray; 14. Seabirds; 15. *Trainspotting*; 16. Médecins Sans Frontières

QUIZ 132

1. Journalism; 2. Eddie Shah; 3. London Eye; 4. Harmonica; 5. Monkey; 6. *The Great Dictator*; 7. Bugs Bunny's; 8. Mercury; 9. Great-granddaughter; 10. 59; 11. Mexico; 12. New Forest; 13. Paul Cézanne; 14. 1839; 15. Julian Lloyd Webber; 16. Pi times radius squared (πr^2)

QUIZ 133

1. Mary Pickford and Douglas Fairbanks'; 2. The *Sun*; 3. Dolores Haze; 4. Restructuring or reconstruction; 5. Sir Thomas Beecham; 6. Crab Key; 7. Colin Meads; 8. Genetically modified; 9. La Mancha; 10. Seven; 11. Athol Fugard; 12. Gene Pitney; 13. Quebec; 14. James Matthew; 15. Smolt; 16. Paul Scofield

QUIZ 134 (Geography)

1. Kirkwall, Orkneys; 2. Tay; 3. Romney Marsh; 4. Loire; 5. Haifa; 6. United Arab Emirates; 7. Congo; 8. Aleutians; 9. Blue and yellow; 10. Large waterfall; 11. Delaware; 12. Mozambique; 13. South Korea; 14. Balboa; 15. Sweden; 16. Australia

QUIZ 135

1. Blue Streak; 2. 116 years; 3. *Billy Budd*; 4. Keyboard; 5. Harold Wilson's; 6. Ambrose Bierce; 7. Pit; 8. Cake; 9. Ireland; 10. Eight (insect); 11. Oliver Cromwell; 12. *The Pearl Fishers* by Georges Bizet; 13. Andy Warhol; 14. Brian Faulkner; 15. 1828; 16. Mah Jong

QUIZ 136

1. Balzac; 2. Towers in the Tower of London; 3. 'The Chicken Song';
4. Jonathan Trott; 5. William Hague; 6. Shakespeare's *Richard III*;
7. Suspenders; 8. Clive of India; 9. 11; 10. Henry Segrave (1923); 11. Ice;
12. Muhammad Ali; 13. Sawalha; 14. Charles Trenet; 15. Dmitry
Medvedev; 16. *Vanity Fair*

QUIZ 137

1. Six months; 2. Devon; 3. Russia; 4. Before the war; 5. Bridge; 6. Carrot;
7. Finished; 8. Doctor of Civil Law; 9. 'Making Your Mind Up'; 10. War of
the Spanish Succession; 11. Swayze; 12. China; 13. Potomac;
14. Alexander Solzhenitsyn; 15. Auckland Castle; 16. Jim Bowie

QUIZ 138

1. Topolino; 2. Backgammon; 3. Ferns; 4. Actress Sarah Bernhardt;
5. Hammersmith; 6. Jimmy Hill; 7. In a plane crash; 8. William Butler;
9. Adam Smith; 10. Wrestling hold; 11. Incisors, canines, molars;
12. Agricultural; 13. Hyde Park; 14. 30 November; 15. Christie Brinkley;
16. Jackfruit

QUIZ 139

1. Father of the House; 2. Angel; 3. Tric Trac; 4. Anne of Cleves;
5. Writer's block; 6. Sir Roger Norrington; 7. White; 8. *Knots Landing*;
9. Italian tomatoes; 10. Austrian; 11. Martha Stewart; 12. Logs;
13. Humorous; 14. Hologram; 15. Bill McLaren; 16. CMXCIX

QUIZ 140

1. Andy Warhol; 2. Song thrush; 3. Martin Clunes; 4. Madonna;
5. Benjamin Britten; 6. Giraffe; 7. Pandora; 8. Pips; 9. Bernard Levin;
10. Dutch; 11. William Thacker; 12. Rosa Parks'; 13. Coniston Water;
14. Jezebel; 15. Salvador Dali; 16. Arquebus

QUIZ 141 (Sport)

1. Gilbert; 2. Kennington Oval; 3. Wanders; 4. Two strokes under par on a hole; 5. Wilhelm Steinitz; 6. A pass thrown deep downfield; 7. Paul Adams (with his contorted bowling action); 8. Trina Gulliver; 9. Rugby league; 10. 14; 11. Cresta Run; 12. Eight; 13. Amongst British Army officers in India; 14. Pat Rice; 15. Ernie Els; 16. Johnny Weissmuller (Tarzan in the movies) won five for swimming

QUIZ 142

1. *Bridget Jones's Diary*; 2. Walk; 3. Rhea Perlman; 4. Eiffel Tower; 5. Darts; 6. The Stars and Stripes; 7. Clermont Club; 8. Two; 9. Robin; 10. Kyoto; 11. Royal flush; 12. Europe; 13. Norman Wisdom's; 14. Broadcasting House; 15. Tiny humanoid creature; 16. Mystic Meg

QUIZ 143

1. Alaska's; 2. Female novelists; 3. Trepanning; 4. Sir Georg Solti; 5. Lynchburg, Tennessee; 6. Marshalsea; 7. Orator; 8. The Spider; 9. Ho Chi Minh; 10. Stirring porridge; 11. Alexander Borodin; 12. Bug; 13. Dick Francis; 14. Sky Peer-to-Peer; 15. Donny Osmond; 16. George W Bush

QUIZ 144

1. Barack Obama; 2. Swiss; 3. 23; 4. Lyndon Johnson's; 5. Alan Shearer; 6. Earl Grey; 7. Boutros Boutros-Ghali; 8. *Hamlet*; 9. Fort Baxter; 10. George IV; 11. Morpheus; 12. Oscar Wilde; 13. Aardvark; 14. Nancy Spungen; 15. 13 tricks by one team; 16. Charlotte

QUIZ 145

1. Pierre Boulle; 2. 28; 3. Albert Einstein; 4. Binnacle; 5. 12; 6. Adolf Hitler; 7. Terry's Old Geezers; 8. Mark Spitz; 9. Estelle Morris; 10. 'I serve'; 11. Huey Long; 12. Balsa; 13. 27; 14. Spiced ham; 15. *Don Quixote*; 16. Organized crime syndicate

QUIZ 146

1. Four; 2. Silver; 3. Libra (scales); 4. James Herbert's; 5. Agent provocateur; 6. Labour (Margaret Bondfield, 1929); 7. Leon Trotsky; 8. Jupiter; 9. Hastings; 10. Judith; 11. Asia; 12. Man overboard; 13. Pepin the Short; 14. Linda Ronstadt; 15. Ben and Casey Affleck; 16. Edward VII

QUIZ 147

1. 1919; 2. Hunter; 3. Dry; 4. Frond; 5. Jean-Paul Marat; 6. The bank at Monte Carlo; 7. Zen; 8. Cinna; 9. Show-jumping obstacle; 10. Yeovilton; 11. Whooping cough; 12. Bysshe; 13. Max Planck; 14. 'Down Down'; 15. Mississippi; 16. Damask

QUIZ 148

1. USA; 2. Demi Moore's and Bruce Willis'; 3. Russia; 4. Bruce Springsteen; 5. Neutron; 6. Vishnu; 7. *Have I Got News For You*; 8. Aruba; 9. Blood-red; 10. Wooded countryside; 11. Perth; 12. Spain; 13. Sandpiper; 14. British Airline Pilots Association; 15. Lancaster; 16. Mike Hammer

QUIZ 149 (Cinema & TV)

1. Detective Sergeant James Hathaway; 2. James Arness; 3. Jets and Sharks; 4. Japanese; 5. Connie Booth; 6. *Se7en*; 7. Portmeirion; 8. *All Quiet on the Western Front*; 9. John McClane; 10. Finlay and Cameron; 11. Judi Dench's (*Shakespeare in Love*); 12. *Marienbad*; 13. Maryland; 14. Dylan; 15. Keiko the whale; 16. Count Basie's

QUIZ 150

1. Woody Boyd; 2. Spice Island; 3. Jacques Offenbach; 4. Wingless insect; 5. Las Vegas; 6. Confetti; 7. George C Scott (for *Patton*); 8. Two; 9. Tadpoles; 10. Hungary; 11. Birds eggs; 12. Bran; 13. *Live and Let Die*; 14. William of Baskerville; 15. Ugandan shilling; 16. 'Love To Love You'

QUIZ 151

1. Plate; 2. Knox and Vivienne; 3. Peter York; 4. Sing Sing prison;

5. Shepherd's Bush; 6. Henrik Ibsen; 7. Joe Calzaghe; 8. Ten; 9. Thomas Jefferson; 10. Toby; 11. Tree; 12. German; 13. Levi Stubbs; 14. Jack Dawson; 15. Pod; 16. 1948

QUIZ 152
1. Jocasta; 2. Emily Brontë; 3. *Beautiful World*; 4. Hell; 5. St Joseph; 6. 1966; 7. Afghani; 8. Ken Ashton; 9. Fudge; 10. Joseph Black; 11. Seymour; 12. Edward Elgar; 13. Absolute zero; 14. Florenz Ziegfeld's; 15. Acts of the Apostles; 16. Zeus

QUIZ 153
1. Won Ton Ton; 2. Stasi; 3. Curtis Cup; 4. Two; 5. Cairn; 6. Bluecoat School; 7. Samaritans; 8. Prince; 9. Cob wall; 10. John Birch Society; 11. Stollen; 12. 'The Ballad Of John And Yoko'; 13. *Eagle*; 14. Taxonomy; 15. Soundtrack of *South Pacific*; 16. Ayrshire

QUIZ 154
1. Twice; 2. Tontons Macoutes; 3. *Slumdog Millionaire*; 4. Horses; 5. Cortes; 6. 11; 7. Mt Vinson; 8. Mikis Theodoraki; 9. Hamlet's; 10. Yellow; 11. Farce; 12. Arthur; 13. *The Jewel of the Nile*; 14. Sir Arthur Harris; 15. Shadowfax; 16. Hawse

QUIZ 155
1. Four; 2. Alabama; 3. Lady Godiva's; 4. Edmonton; 5. 1927; 6. Pablo Picasso's; 7. Punishment; 8. *Dr No*; 9. Nine; 10. Newfoundland; 11. Ivan the Terrible (Ivan IV); 12. Upkeep; 13. Hawaii; 14. Red beret; 15. Equity; 16. Stern Gang

QUIZ 156 (Science & Nature)
1. Richard Dawkins; 2. Hay fever; 3. Euclid; 4. Colour blindness; 5. Red; 6. Minus 18°; 7. Rheology; 8. Pipistrelle; 9. Cornea; 10. Millions of Instructions Per Second; 11. Eight; 12. An asteroid; 13. Fast breeder reactor; 14. Mosses; 15. Tapeworm; 16. Craters on the Moon

QUIZ 157

1. (Dr) Brian Cox; 2. 24; 3. The *Observer*; 4. Scotland; 5. The Bronx (New York); 6. Judah; 7. Confucious; 8. To pass a point of no return; 9. Teddy boys and girls; 10. Rudyard Kipling; 11. Mike Oldfield; 12. Monica Seles; 13. 'A Whole New World'; 14. Kevin Spacey; 15. Lake Ontario; 16. Major Boothroyd

QUIZ 158

1. Five; 2. A R Rahman; 3. Because of the frilly underwear she wore on court; 4. 1951; 5. 32; 6. Thomas More; 7. Daphne Du Maurier's; 8. Cleo Laine; 9. Green; 10. Paris Hilton's (*The Tinkerbell Hilton Diaries*); 11. PSV Eindhoven; 12. Eternal President; 13. Bolivia; 14. Sirte; 15. Prickly plant; 16. Billie Holiday

QUIZ 159

1. Let; 2. 1904; 3. Burlap; 4. US Marine Corps; 5. 'Always faithful'; 6. *The Wizard of Oz*; 7. Ronnie Scott; 8. St Valentine's; 9. Cointreau; 10. Vidkun Quisling; 11. Off the coast of northern Australia; 12. Cato; 13. Saxophone; 14. Computers; 15. Florence Griffith-Joyner; 16. Klaus Barbie

QUIZ 160

1. Formentera; 2. Czechoslovakia; 3. Florence; 4. Guy Mitchell, Tommy Steele and Marty Robbins; 5. John Huston; 6. Japanese flower arranging; 7. Cadel Evans; 8. Lord Tweedsmuir; 9. Marlon Brando; 10. Royal Observatory, Greenwich; 11. Tiki; 12. Carson City; 13. Cluricauns; 14. USA v Canada (1844); 15. Jules Massenet; 16. Latest fashion

QUIZ 161

1. Skopje; 2. Michelangelo's; 3. Light Amplification by Stimulated Emission of Radiation; 4. Mork Turtle; 5. Beverley; 6. Rameses the Great; 7. Eastern Cape; 8. Robert Aldrich; 9. Pole vault; 10. Soya beans;

11. Dudley Moore; 12. Jimmy Hill; 13. Leopold Stokowski;
14. Gooseberry; 15. Historians; 16. Adam Faith

QUIZ 162
1. With authority; 2. L S Lowry; 3. Sue Perkins; 4. Quinine; 5. Sapphire;
6. Mozambique and Tanzania; 7. Garry Sobers; 8. Sir Mordred; 9. In a
plane crash; 10. Flying Doctor Service; 11. Egypt; 12. Monsoon;
13. Long sidewhiskers; 14. Dido; 15. The Battery; 16. Richard Strauss

QUIZ 163
1. Bernard Madoff; 2. Angry Brigade; 3. Ultramarine; 4. Everton Weekes;
5. Coffee bar; 6. Gambia; 7. Netherlands; 8. John Clare; 9. No Doubt;
10. Medici; 11. Cusack; 12. Western Australian Cricket Association;
13. Holt; 14. Tyrrhenian Sea; 15. Suffolk; 16. Ernest Borgnine

QUIZ 164 (Music)
1. Rebecca; 2. Lulu; 3. Poland; 4. 36; 5. 'Sloop John B'; 6. Sir Hubert Parry;
7. Prince Buster; 8. Vampire Weekend's; 9. Adele; 10. Maya Angelou;
11. Cliff Richard; 12. Mis-Teeq; 13. Luther Vandross; 14. *The Thomas
Crown Affair*; 15. Vivaldi; 16. Nine

QUIZ 165
1. Jimmy Carter's; 2. Witches Sabbath; 3. Mochica; 4. Bile; 5. Barbara
Hepworth; 6. 50-59; 7. Mel Gibson's; 8. Antarctica; 9. 1929; 10. Mikado;
11. Cumbria; 12. Martlet 13. Six; 14. Junta; 15. John Stonehouse;
16. Opera singer

QUIZ 166
1. Hereward the Wake; 2. Sir Arthur Quiller-Couch's; 3. Strait of
Magellan; 4. Citadel or fortress; 5. Metropolitan Line; 6. Pasture pigs in a
forest; 7. 14; 8. Bruce Grobbelaar; 9. New Zealand; 10. North Atlantic;
11. Barney and Betty Rubble's in *The Flintstones*; 12. Smut; 13. Aeolian
Harp; 14. Grip; 15. Robin Hood; 16. Pencil

QUIZ 167

1. 'Seize the day'; 2. Theseus; 3. *César*; 4. Persian Gulf and Gulf of Oman;
5. Katherine Anne Porter; 6. Hieronymus Bosch; 7. Colon; 8. Conifer;
9. Mariah Carey and Whitney Houston; 10. The Oval; 11. Left;
12. Norman Scott; 13. Willow; 14. Daniel Fahrenheit's; 15. Let's just be
friends; 16. William Rushton

QUIZ 168

1. Less; 2. Black Sea; 3. Malaria; 4. Mother Teresa; 5. Dolly Varden;
6. Adam Faith; 7. Cockatrice; 8. 12 minutes; 9. Daniel Defoe; 10. One
thousand; 11. William I; 12. Peru; 13. Benjamin Franklin; 14. 'Christmas Is
All Around'; 15. Nanjing; 16. Beauty

QUIZ 169

1. 1926; 2. Winston Churchill; 3. 'Blue Christmas'; 4. Joe Frazier; 5. Wells;
6. Didier Drogba; 7. George Bush; 8. Tines; 9. Eden Project; 10. National
People's Congress; 11. Salzburg; 12. Four; 13. Architect; 14. Sauternes;
15. Oscar Kokoschka; 16. Billy Connolly

QUIZ 170

1. *Strasse*; 2. Norfolk; 3. Brassica; 4. Arrow; 5. Albert Einstein; 6. Giant ape;
7. Five; 8. Picts; 9. Devil's Island; 10. One; 11. George Michael's;
12. 18th Century; 13. Lullaby; 14. Sir Henry Cotton's; 15. Golden apple;
16. Pears soap

QUIZ 171 (History)

1. A J P Tayler; 2. Richard Cromwell; 3. General Sherman; 4. George III's;
5. 1967; 6. Thomas Cranmer; 7. My Lai; 8. Napoleon III; 9. St Francis of
Assisi; 10. Ramsay MacDonald; 11. Iceni; 12. The Black Prince; 13. An
Englishman named Edward Teach; 14. John F Kennedy; 15. *Alexander
Kielland*; 16. Rev Jim Jones

QUIZ 172

1. Dr Edward Fitzgerald; 2. Two; 3. Dr David Kelly; 4. Rain; 5. The Goodies;
6. Arctic; 7. Four; 8. Nick Faldo; 9. State of the Union; 10. 39; 11. 1000;
12. Reaching the summit of Mt Everest; 13. Bastet; 14. Bob Marley's;
15. Drupe; 16. Fabien Pelous

QUIZ 173

1. +48; 2. Eye; 3. Teofilo Stevenson; 4. Left; 5. Hermes; 6. 'The
Turbanator'; 7. Thar Desert; 8. The Buggles; 9. Apple; 10. Dandelion;
11. Fotheringhay Castle; 12. It ended up a five-way tie; 13. *Turandot*;
14. Adit; 15. Ted Hughes; 16. Heart of Midlothian

QUIZ 174

1. Norman Tebbit; 2. Phonetic; 3. True; 4. Richard Hadlee; 5. *The Day of
the Locust*; 6. Nathanael West's; 7. Jessica; 8. Black eagle; 9. Bob Dylan;
10. Jewish mystics; 11. Gareth Thomas; 12. Make and repair shoes;
13. Jackie Jackson; 14. People's Republic of the Congo; 15. George
Formby's; 16. Fluke

QUIZ 175

1. Al Qaeda's; 2. 31; 3. Robert the Bruce; 4. Two; 5. Grey Gables;
6. P Diddy; 7. Flags; 8. Bird; 9. Schuhplattler; 10. *King Kong*; 11. Duffy's;
12. Potato; 13. *The Kursk*; 14. Robert Browning; 15. 18; 16. Canada's

QUIZ 176

1. Railway station; 2. 1994; 3. A L Kennedy; 4. Brazilian; 5. Ba'ath Party;
6. Edward Heath (1973); 7. Jerry Garcia; 8. 'Have a nice day'; 9. Boris
Becker (1985); 10. Michael Curtiz; 11. Pony; 12. Lord Melbourne;
13. Became a hotel in Dubai; 14. Howard Hughes; 15. Jonathan King;
16. *My Own Private Idaho*

QUIZ 177

1. Pembroke Castle; 2. Black; 3. Jack Aubrey; 4. His son Jason; 5. Pam Dawber; 6. Crocodile; 7. John Philip Sousa; 8. Malaria; 9. Blenheim Palace; 10. Henry Ford; 11. Bowls; 12. Sir Percy Blakeney; 13. Madeleine Albright; 14. Donald Neilson; 15. Snow pellets; 16. Muster

QUIZ 178

1. 1982; 2. Knight Commander of the Royal Victorian Order; 3. Omar Sharif; 4. 1948 touring side to England; 5. 1914; 6. Motherboard; 7. Napoleon Bonaparte; 8. Openness; 9. 35; 10. UK foreign secretary's; 11. *The Adventures of Huckleberry Finn*; 12. Sculpture; 13. Rio Ferdinand; 14. Haiti; 15. Obadiah; 16. 10,080

QUIZ 179 (Geography)

1. Port Moresby; 2. Chile; 3. Italy; 4. Grand Canal of China; 5. Chimney; 6. Swansea; 7. Strait of Gibraltar; 8. Spree; 9. Portuguese; 10. China and Mongolia; 11. La Paz (Bolivia); 12. Indonesia; 13. St Petersburg; 14. Volcano; 15. Gourde; 16. London

QUIZ 180

1. Portsmouth; 2. 49; 3. Latrine; 4. Fish; 5. Dr Richard Beeching's; 6. Paul Weller; 7. Satyr; 8. Wilson; 9. Kerosene; 10. Wilfred Owen; 11. Dr Douglas Ross; 12. A S Byatt; 13. Landscape gardener; 14. Martini; 15. Mesolithic; 16. Tottenham Hotspur

QUIZ 181

1. Sonny Liston; 2. Whitbury New Town; 3. 1979; 4. Susan; 5. Sylvia Plath; 6. Bedrich Smetana; 7. Brogdale (Kent); 8. Meteor showers; 9. Canadian; 10. Albatross; 11. Diabetes; 12. Chamonix (1924); 13. Lech Walesa; 14. Meat Loaf's *Bat Out Of Hell*; 15. Alder wood; 16. Franz Joseph Haydn

QUIZ 182

1. Richie Cunningham; 2. Hereford Cathedral; 3. Aphrodite; 4. Venus;
5. Cribbage; 6. Rodent; 7. 11; 8. Westerns; 9. Maracanã; 10. Three;
11. Scalene; 12. *The Mysterious Affair at Styles*; 13. 50m; 14. Formic acid;
15. Amber; 16. Red, white and blue

QUIZ 183

1. *The Big Sleep*; 2. Nagoya Grampus Eight; 3. Rainbow Bridge; 4. Pecking
order; 5. Crimean War; 6. 'Unchained Melody'; 7. George V's;
8. East; 9. Rod Laver; 10. +30; 11. 1783; 12. Satchmo (Louis Armstrong);
13. Trondheim; 14. *To Kill a Mocking Bird*; 15. Fairyhouse; 16. June

QUIZ 184

1.Majorie Dawes ; 2. Norwich Cathedral; 3. Finland; 4. Green; 5. Milan;
6. Thabo Mbeke; 7. Trombone; 8. Grand Union; 9. Travelling companion;
10. Ostrich; 11. *The Little Prince*; 12. Clint Eastwood; 13. Fish; 14. John
Standing; 15. British monarch's; 16. Brooklands (Surrey)

QUIZ 185

1. Chocolate, vanilla and strawberry; 2. Uranus; 3. *Dick Tracy*; 4. Nobel
Peace Prize; 5. C P Snow; 6. Japanese sandals; 7. Phyllis Nelson;
8. Arthur Ransome; 9. Stephen Fry; 10. Genoa; 11. Willy Loman (*Death of
a Salesman*); 12. Cherry (nicknamed 'The Cherries'); 13. *Hollyoaks*;
14. Starfish; 15. Woolloongabba (Brisbane); 16. Mt Kailash

QUIZ 186 (Sport)

1. Australia; 2. St Leger; 3. Sir Pelham Warner; 4. 15; 5. Bobby Campbell;
6. Race Across America; 7. Coventry City; 8. Hockenheim; 9. American
football; 10. Turnberry; 11. Passivity zone; 12. New Zealand; 13. Golf;
14. Alan Border; 15. 49; 16. Ferguson

QUIZ 187

1. They reduce cholesterol; 2. *Blade Runner*; 3. Isle of Man; 4. Red;
5. Morkel; 6. Daniel Day-Lewis; 7. Mockney; 8. Pam Ayres; 9. Warren
Beatty; 10. 1997; 11. George Frederick Handel; 12. Spitz; 13. 30;
14. Alba; 15. American Football; 16. Winston

QUIZ 188

1. Smarties; 2. Stream; 3. Shinto; 4. Grand Old Duke of York; 5. 1958;
6. Iodine; 7. Johnny Chan; 8. Victoria Wood's; 9. Three; 10. Bill Lawry;
11. Midge Ure; 12. Noise Abatement Society; 13. J M W Turner;
14. Richard Doyle; 15. Moorcock; 16. Hercule Poirot

QUIZ 189

1. Benjamin Disraeli; 2. Chairs; 3. *Hollyoaks*; 4. Apron; 5. Henry James;
6. Social housing; 7. Roger Taylor; 8. Female; 9. Penguin; 10. Max
Bygraves'; 11. In prison; 12. Beelzebub; 13. Sir John Moore; 14. Sir John
Moores; 15. Lady Gaga; 16. Stag

QUIZ 190

1. Nonet; 2. Homer Simpson; 3. Victor; 4. Salvation Army's;
5. Tchaikovsky; 6. Cow; 7. Westlife's; 8. Michael Moore; 9. Congo;
10. Fritillary; 11. Sunil Gavaskar; 12. *Carrie*; 13. Mathematics; 14. Pays
Basque; 15. 16th; 16. James Thomson

QUIZ 191

1. Piers Morgan; 2. -40°; 3. Antonia Fraser and Harold Pinter; 4. Seven;
5. Trumpet; 6. *Alien*; 7. New York city; 8. Marjorie Proops; 9. National
Hunt; 10. Psychiatry; 11. Kama; 12. 1984; 13. Milkman; 14. C B Fry's;
15. Prague; 16. Anne Brontë

QUIZ 192

1. Segway; 2. The Who; 3. Jenny; 4. St Vitus (St Vitus' Dance); 5. 'Diamond
Lights'; 6. Margaret Thatcher; 7. 1857; 8. *Sayonara*; 9. £2 (1946);

10. Rembrandt; 11. Glynis Johns; 12. Gaia; 13. Zirconium; 14. New Albion; 15. Tim Rice; 16. Hugh Carleton Greene (brother of Graham Greene)

QUIZ 193
1. Turkey; 2. Cassandra; 3. Bar; 4. Richard III; 5. 1969; 6. Swan Upping; 7. Sergei Prokofiev; 8. Teleprinter Exchange; 9. Four; 10. Alfred Harmsworth (Lord Northcliffe); 11. Flock of sheep; 12. Garry Kasparov; 13. Egyptian vulture; 14. J K Rowling; 15. Harry Houdini; 16. Argentina

QUIZ 194 (Cinema & TV)
1. *All About Eve*; 2. Six; 3. *The Office*; 4. Ridley and Tony Scott; 5. Dooley Wilson; 6. Ainsley Harriott; 7. Astro; 8. David Lean; 9. *Man About the House*; 10. Paul McGann; 11. Fox; 12. *Heart of Darkness* (Joseph Conrad); 13. *A Bronx Tale*; 14. Wilfred Brambell; 15. Veronica Lake; 16. Cate Blanchett, Nicole Kidman, Russell Crowe, Geoffrey Rush

QUIZ 195
1. Richard Nixon; 2. *William*; 3. John McEnroe; 4. Twice sold; 5. Bedrich; 6. Zinedine Zidane; 7. Empty orchestra; 8. Sri Lanka; 9. Prophetess; 10. Annie Nightingale; 11. *Hindenburg*; 12. Bhutan; 13. Jeff Banks (*The Clothes Show*); 14. Blue; 15. Gustave Flaubert; 16. Kite

QUIZ 196
1. Marlon Brando; 2. Battleship *Potemkin*; 3. Tenerife; 4. Lemuel; 5. Flying boat; 6. Left; 7. Lothar Matthäus; 8. Zeppo; 9. Nile; 10. Drum; 11. San Francisco; 12. Henry; 13. Maiden; 14. Ham; 15. Joshua Slocum; 16. On a beach in the Virgin Island of St John

QUIZ 197
1. Robert Catesby; 2. Oxford; 3. Girth; 4. Scaffold; 5. Silk; 6. *Crime and Punishment*; 7. Plover; 8. Horse; 9. Clytemnestra; 10. Matthew Hayden; 11. Richmond; 12. Manchester United; 13. The Kumars; 14. 1947; 15. Chuck Yeager; 16. Holly Johnson

QUIZ 198

1. Frangipani; 2. Exodus; 3. Antonia Fraser; 4. Chutzpah; 5. 10cc; 6. Arrow maker; 7. St Sebastian; 8. Alexander Pope; 9. Oxford; 10. Steve Fossett; 11. 71; 12. Lament; 13. Captain Marvel; 14. Eight; 15. Brasilia; 16. Sleeve

QUIZ 199

1. Birmingham; 2. Dashiell Hammett; 3. Broken wrist; 4. 17th; 5. Ireland; 6. Warsaw Pact; 7. Indonesia's; 8. Four; 9. Crassus; 10. With poison; 11. Night; 12. Granite; 13. Dandy Nichols; 14. Marcus Trescothick's; 15. Al Gore's *An Inconvenient Truth*; 16. Clam shell

QUIZ 200

1. Flower; 2. Charlie Chaplin; 3. Ivor the Engine's driver; 4. *Diana and Actaeon*; 5. Aberdeen; 6. Euphrates and Tigris; 7. New York; 8. Frank Marcus; 9. Zeus; 10. 1967; 11. Gladys Knight; 12. Robert Southey; 13. Nanjing; 14. Eminem; 15. Cambridge; 16. An imam

QUIZ 201 (Science & Nature)

1. Smack; 2. One; 3. Fish; 4. Bees (Bee Eater); 5. Diplodocus; 6. Cheshire; 7. Daisy-like flower; 8. Indivisible; 9. Aerodynamics; 10. Brain; 11. Test-tube baby; 12. Hardness of minerals; 13. Mauritius; 14. Being alone; 15. Foxglove; 16. Seven Sisters

QUIZ 202

1. Gateshead; 2. Great Auk; 3. Sachin Tendulkar; 4. Captain Queeg; 5. Thames; 6. Balsam; 7. The Kills; 8. Boxer Bob Fitzsimmons (1902); 9. Amritsar; 10. George Washington; 11. William Thackeray's; 12. Mt Elbrus; 13. New Jersey; 14. Manuel de Falla; 15. Mustique; 16. *The Blues Brothers*

QUIZ 203

1. Osprey; 2. André Breton; 3. 1976; 4. Harry Webb; 5. Konrad Adenauer; 6. USA; 7. Queen Victoria; 8. Boar; 9. Barley and water; 10. Christopher Chataway; 11. Witty remark; 12. 1954; 13. Frank Sinatra; 14. K2;

15. Elizabeth Jane Howard; 16. Great Ormond Street Hospital

QUIZ 204

1. Barrow; 2. USA; 3. Buttercup; 4. Imelda Marcos; 5. Bolivia; 6. Trevor Immelman; 7. Jethro Tull; 8. Celtic; 9. General Mark Clark; 10. Blood pressure; 11. Ajaccio; 12. Freshwater; 13. *The Brothers Karamazov*; 14. *Brittanic*; 15. Group Captain Leonard Cheshire; 16. John F Kennedy

QUIZ 205

1. Cricket; 2. Voluntary Aid Detachment; 3. *Middlemarch*; 4. Pauline Collins; 5. Tommy Simpson; 6. Veneto; 7. Association of Tennis Professionals; 8. Warren Harding; 9. 'Desire'; 10. Poker; 11. Robert the Bruce; 12. She Who Must Be Obeyed; 13. Montenegro; 14. Copenhagen; 15. Scarborough; 16. Sir Lancelot

QUIZ 206

1. Thrush; 2. *Paradise Regained*; 3. San Marino; 4. Paul Revere's; 5. New Zealand; 6. Portland Vase; 7. Keir Hardie; 8. Lewisham; 9. Nik Kershaw; 10. Nobel Prize in Literature (1909); 11. Will Carling's; 12. Polish; 13. Bacchus; 14. Moldavia; 15. Yucatan; 16. Asteroids

QUIZ 207

1. *A Hitchhiker's Guide to the Galaxy*; 2. The Factory; 3. Theodore Roosevelt; 4. Frans Hals; 5. Royal Horse Guards; 6. Bill Wyman; 7. One and a half miles (2.4 Km); 8. Volcanic island; 9. Finland's; 10. Wig; 11. Sheena Easton; 12. Croquet; 13. Pfeiffer; 14. Jester; 15. One; 16. Diamond shaped

QUIZ 208 (Music)

1. Singer; 2. British; 3. *Kid Galahad*; 4. 21; 5. The Chemical Brothers; 6. Capella; 7. John Lennon and the Plastic Ono Band; 8. Franz Joseph Haydn; 9. Bob Dylan; 10. The Rain; 11. Jarvis Cocker; 12. Plane crash; 13. Banana; 14. Tom Jones; 15. Richard Clayderman; 16. 'Happy Birthday To You'

QUIZ 209

1. Tim Minchin; 2. Vladimir Kramnik; 3. Mahjong; 4. Virginia; 5. Germany;
6. Exeter; 7. Poseidon; 8. Shania Twain; 9. Ants; 10. Arthur; 11. Sculptor;
12. Charles II; 13. Elton John; 14. Nauru; 15. Gustav Klimt; 16. Jennie Lee

QUIZ 210

1. Japan; 2. Auk; 3. Mrs Mary Whitehouse; 4. John Ross; 5. Edward Gibbon;
6. Witham; 7. Charles; 8. 16; 9. Trees; 10. Dan Maskell; 11. David Soul;
12. Tonga; 13. Type of guitar; 14. Danforth; 15. *Daily Telegraph*; 16. John
Landy

QUIZ 211

1. Kingfisher; 2. Joseph Kennedy; 3. Rabindranath Tagore; 4. Your
Eminence; 5. SALT-2; 6. Cyclops; 7. 1999; 8. Honshu; 9. Steve Jobs;
10. Toulouse-Lautrec's; 11. Bear; 12. Left; 13. Black; 14. Jordan's;
15. Damon Runyan's; 16. 'It's Now Or Never'

QUIZ 212

1. Jeremy Beadle; 2. Neil Tennant; 3. In secret; 4. Raphael Selbourne;
5. Magistrate; 6. Magpie; 7. Lord Mountbatten; 8. Coventry; 9. Five;
10. Cross Fell; 11. Mast; 12. White City; 13. Red Hot Chili Peppers;
14. Mary Hopkin; 15. Stella Gibbons; 16. Richard Nixon

QUIZ 213

1. Grandson-in-law; 2. Policemen; 3. Male head of a household;
4. Christopher Sholes; 5. Berlin (1936); 6. Chevrolet; 7. Comic (1884);
8. Delon and Steffon; 9. Carbon; 10. Barrington Pheloung; 11. Frank
Lloyd Wright; 12. Ten; 13. Jimmie Rodgers; 14. Sheridan; 15. Exmoor
ponies; 16. Tweetie Pie

QUIZ 214

1. Somerset; 2. Elizabeth Barrett Browning's; 3. Zimbabwe African

National Union - Patriotic Front; 4. Yoko Ono's; 5. Pince-nez;
6. Simon Callow; 7. 'Waterloo'; 8. 16; 9. Lizard; 10. Earth; 11. Marshall
McLuhan; 12. St Jude's Institute; 13. Goya; 14. Tunisia; 15. Photography;
16. 17

QUIZ 215

1. Jerusalem; 2. Michael Morpurgo; 3. Four-footed animal; 4. Edward
Heath; 5. On their ears (earrings); 6. 'MacArthur Park'; 7. BAMBI Awards;
8. Table tennis; 9. Raul Castro; 10. Drunk in public; 11. Sn; 12. Chopsticks;
13. Auric; 14. Doctor of Laws; 15. Cor anglais; 16. Renaissance

QUIZ 216 (History)

1. Malayan Emergency; 2. Marie Louise of Austria; 3. The Commonwealth
of England (1649–60); 4. Citizen's Charter; 5. 1949; 6. 92; 7. King Idris;
8. Macbeth; 9. 1849; 10. Mahatma Gandhi; 11. Salvador Allende;
12. General James Wolfe; 13. Paddy Ashdown; 14. Anastasia;
15. Ibn Saud; 16. Deng Xiaoping

QUIZ 217

1. *Turn Off the Dark*; 2. Bono and The Edge; 3. Canute; 4. 25; 5. *The Ed
Sullivan Show*; 6. Maine; 7. Three; 8. *Jude the Obscure*; 9. Campbell;
10. Anthea Redfern; 11. Cistine Chapel; 12. Cello; 13. Westward Ho!;
14. Julian Fellowes; 15. Richard Wagner; 16. Marni Nixon

QUIZ 218

1. Both (he was ambidextrous); 2. Equally clumsy with both hands;
3. Hunk (the hired man); 4. Ray Bolger; 5. *Where's Waldo?*; 6. North
Island; 7. 1980; 8. Leprosy; 9. Germany and Italy; 10. Monkey;
11. William Pitt (the elder); 12. Anne Robinson's; 13. Alan Knott;
14. Wonder Woman; 15. George Martin (their producer); 16. Simone
Signoret

QUIZ 219

1. Brian Epstein; 2. Monolith; 3. A E Housman; 4. Basso profundo;
5. Simon de Montfort; 6. Mrs Beeton; 7. *Meet Me in St Louis*; 8. Chappell-
Hadlee Trophy; 9. Ospreys; 10. Arnold Wesker; 11. Iceberg; 12. William L
Shirer; 13. Ruthie Henshall; 14. Marco Materazzi; 15. Blackwall; 16. B-52s

QUIZ 220

1. Sir Arnold Wesker; 2. Henry Morton; 3. Gareth Keenan; 4. Australia;
5. Pork Pie hat; 6. Crystal Palace; 7. Tim Rice; 8. Greyhound;
9. 'Unfinished'; 10. Structure of DNA; 11. Taken without owner's
consent; 12. *The Posthumous Papers of the Pickwick Club*; 13. Lemur;
14. Madagascar; 15. Music journalist; 16. Lancashire

QUIZ 221

1. Page; 2. YMCA; 3. Bob Charles; 4. Renault; 5. Otters; 6. Milky Way;
7. Sean Penn; 8. Chicken; 9. Robert Morse; 10. Hackle; 11. Scotland;
12. Trilby; 13. 1981; 14. Beware of the dog!; 15. Sixth; 16. Comforter

QUIZ 222

1. Three; 2. *Apache*; 3. Sloane Square; 4. George Lazenby; 5. Broiling;
6. Piano; 7. Princess Michael of Kent; 8. Swim (fish); 9. Torture device;
10. Amy Johnson; 11. Film production; 12. Oxford and Cambridge;
13. Rupert Murdoch; 14. Colorado; 15. Neil Diamond; 16. Alexander
Pushkin's

QUIZ 223

1. 1960; 2. Julia Ward Howe; 3. Pygmalion; 4. Jochen Rindt (who died
earlier in the season but never lost his lead); 5. Captain Langsdorff;
6. Peter Finch; 7. William Saroyan; 8. Dumb waiter; 9. Panama hat;
10. Anna Pavlova's; 11. Phiz; 12. Orenthal James; 13. 'Goodbye'; 14. Type
of grass; 15. Prince Edward; 16. Sitwell

QUIZ 224 (Geography)

1. Sierra Nevada; 2. Area of shifting sand dunes; 3. Jersey; 4. Liberia;
5. Botswana; 6. Cyprus; 7. Niger; 8. Barents Sea; 9. Cairo; 10. South Korea;
11. Avenue of the Americas; 12. Atacama Desert (Chile); 13. Latvia;
14. Cayenne; 15. Greenland; 16. Mount Athos

QUIZ 225

1. *Good Wives*; 2. Four; 3. Topee; 4. O J Simpson; 5. Dog licence; 6. Major
Pat Reid; 7. Six; 8. Leveret; 9. Sir Stamford Raffles; 10. Tower of Babel;
11. In the act of a crime; 12. 1985; 13. Dromedary; 14. Word; 15. Joel
Cairo; 16. 'New flower'

QUIZ 226

1. Richard Branson and Per Lindstrand; 2. Margate; 3. Mammal;
4. Hereford Cathedral; 5. Kathy Burke; 6. Workshop or studio;
7. By cutting the turf; 8. Bob Geldof; 9. 1973; 10. Mexico; 11. Ben
Kingsley's; 12. Florida; 13. Dr Dolittle; 14. French; 15. Pullover; 16. Giraffe

QUIZ 227

1. 'Sound mind in a healthy body'; 2. Ox; 3. Arlington; 4. Pilton Festival;
5. Saturn; 6. William Pitt (the younger); 7. Donkey; 8. *Deepwater Horizon*;
9. *The Mystery of Edwin Drood*; 10. Edwina; 11. Elgin Marbles; 12. Inca;
13. James Goldsmith; 14. Hurling; 15. White; 16. Jasper Carrott

QUIZ 228

1. Screen; 2. *Daily Mail*; 3. *Catch-22*; 4. Prince Albert (husband of Queen
Victoria); 5. Mississippi; 6. *The Spectator*; 7. Trampolining; 8. The first
paying passenger in Space; 9. Carlsberg; 10. *Kon-Tiki*; 11. Meg Ryan;
12. South Dakota; 13. Charterhouse; 14. Dr Bunsen Honeydew; 15. Nine;
16. Bleeding

QUIZ 229

1. Female; 2. Very dry; 3. MCMLXXVII (1977); 4. *Two Greedy Italians*;
5. Ginger; 6. Saw timber; 7. Doris Day; 8. Vaduz; 9. *The Big Issue*;
10. Woodstock; 11. Melted-down rupees; 12. Ridley Scott; 13. China's;
14. Gill; 15. Phil and Don; 16. Snake

QUIZ 230

1. Pan Am; 2. *Grand cru*; 3. Laurie Lee; 4. Greek musical instrument;
5. Russia; 6. Prithee; 7. Caernarfon Castle; 8. George Washington;
9. De Havilland Comet; 10. West Ham FC; 11. Hale and Pace;
12. Spanish-American; 13. Kyle; 14. Tooth cavities; 15. Amsterdam;
16. Puissance

QUIZ 231 (Sport)

1. Dan Wheldon; 2. Allan Border; 3. Thierry Dusautoir; 4. Jean-Claude
Killy; 5. Harrow School; 6. James Hunt; 7. Mark Philippoussis; 8. Wayne
Rooney; 9. Napier (NZ); 10. Hollioake; 11. Cycling; 12. Jersey Joe
Walcott's; 13. Ron Atkinson; 14. Tom Finney; 15. France; 16. Claire Tayler

QUIZ 232

1. Quentin Crisp; 2. Alan Freeman; 3. *Vis-à-vis*; 4. Finnish; 5. Jackass;
6. Lily; 7. John Major; 8. Proverb or maxim; 9. Australia; 10. Harrier;
11. Alexander Litvinenko; 12. Tallahassee; 13. Bjork; 14. Botany;
15. Shirley Bassey; 16. 37 minutes

QUIZ 233

1. M6; 2. Charles Darwin's; 3. Champagne; 4. Potassium; 5. Skiff; 6. Twice
a month; 7. Strawweight; 8. Gringo; 9. Bismarck; 10. Girls; 11. Drum;
12. 1986; 13. *Battlestar Galactica*; 14. Newfoundland; 15. Cars;
16. Peter Gabriel

QUIZ 234

1. France; 2. Staffordshire; 3. Cellulose; 4. Ludo; 5. Philadelphia;
6. Shamrock; 7. *The Exorcist*; 8. Zone Improvement Plan; 9. Chicago;
10. Wellington; 11. Libretto; 12. Twilight; 13. A player backed by
someone else; 14. Principality; 15. Glasgow; 16. Lakes and ponds

QUIZ 235

1. James Hunt; 2. Benjamin Franklin; 3. F R Spofforth (1879); 4. Barack
Obama's; 5. Geri Halliwell; 6. Lascars; 7. Ian Woosnam; 8. 120km/h
(75mph); 9. Great Bitter Lake; 10. Joan Sutherland; 11. Rachel Johnson;
12. Penguin; 13. Horace Greeley; 14. Pig Hill; 15. 'To a Field Mouse'
(Robert Burns); 16. Leo Sayer

QUIZ 236

1. Half-crown; 2. Greg Dyke; 3. Bronco; 4. Phoebe's grandmother's;
5. Blood pressure; 6. Green Paper; 7. Herbert Morrison; 8. Nirvana;
9. *Amoco Cadiz*; 10. Large bay; 11. Lebanon's; 12. Gridiron; 13. 9.30pm;
14. Stacy Keach; 15. Presidential Medal of Freedom; 16. Danbert
Nobacon of Chumbawamba

QUIZ 237

1. *Piper Alpha*; 2. Adam Crozier; 3. Archery; 4. John Nash; 5. None, but she
was nominated twice; 6. Clarence House; 7. Daedalus; 8. Its proboscis;
9. Types of betting in roulette; 10. Sir Gordon Richards; 11. 30; 12. The
number 10 raised to the power 100; 13. Sheryl Crow; 14. Costa Rica's;
15. Eric Porter; 16. Turkey

QUIZ 238

1. Adam Smith; 2. Red; 3. Agony aunt; 4. HMS *Astute*; 5. Raisa Gorbachev;
6. King of Hearts; 7. Blowfly (Bluebottle); 8. Six (1.8m); 9. Cowdrey;
10. *The Fast Show*; 11. Vatican City; 12. Elmer Bernstein; 13. Yes;
14. Nicaragua; 15. Aluminium; 16. Herschelle Gibbs

QUIZ 239 (Cinema & TV)

1. *A Certain Sacrifice*; 2. John Osborne; 3. De Mooi; 4. Ben Elton; 5. Chris Columbus; 6. Jim Carter; 7. Jeremy Irons'; 8. Bret McKenzie; 9. Keira Knightley; 10. Peggy Olson; 11. Sue Lyon; 12. Rooney Mara; 13. Lisbeth Salander; 14. Dr Gillespie; 15. Huston (Walter, John, Angelica); 16. Keanu Reeves

QUIZ 240

1. Inverness; 2. Crew cuts; 3. Elena Ceausescu (Romania); 4. Grass; 5. Rear suspension; 6. Royal Oak (Charles II hid in an oak tree after the Battle of Worcester); 7. Lovat; 8. Alan Mullery (1968); 9. The White Rabbit; 10. Glen Lyon; 11. Dogfish; 12. Cards in a Tarot pack; 13. Sicily; 14. New York state; 15. Lt Col Herbert Jones; 16. Otis Redding

QUIZ 241

1. Sir Peter Maxwell Davis; 2. Farthing; 3. Card games; 4. India and Pakistan; 5. 'Rabbit' (in John Updike's novels); 6. Grizzly Bear; 7. Its bark; 8. British policemen; 9. The Rape of the Sabine Women; 10. Women's (12 as opposed to 10); 11. Eight; 12. Rum; 13. Madrid; 14. The Weather Girls; 15. Zodiac Killer (never caught); 16. Cotentin

QUIZ 242

1. Alexander Hamilton's; 2. HandMade Films; 3. *Sans-culottes*; 4. Without knee breeches; 5. James Earl Jones; 6. Timothy McVeigh; 7. Mexico; 8. David Irving; 9. Beethoven; 10. Leo Tolstoy; 11. Boy George; 12. Richard III; 13. Laurent Blanc (Fr); 14. 1998 v Paraguay; 15. Little Boots; 16. Yalu

QUIZ 243

1. Royal Anglian; 2. Saddles; 3. Ross; 4. The Patriarch; 5. Linda Tripp; 6. Item of Scottish headwear; 7. Sweet chestnut; 8. Isle of Man; 9. Rose DeWitt Bukater; 10. Paris; 11. 35; 12. San Sebastian; 13. Australian; 14. Sydney's; 15. Elephant; 16. Dee Caffari

QUIZ 244

1. Ancient Chinese; 2. Mecca; 3. Oxford Brookes University; 4. Lord-Lieutenant; 5. New Zealand; 6. Alexandrina; 7. Muhammad Ali; 8. Hot; 9. *Trilby*; 10. George du Maurier; 11. *The Gondoliers*; 12. 50; 13. Sepal; 14. *Oliver's Story*; 15. Gorillaz; 16. Eel

QUIZ 245

1. His terrier, Caesar; 2. James Franco and Anne Hathaway; 3. Crown Prince Constantine (of Greece); 4. Sphagnum; 5. Capt John Ridgway and Sgt Chay Blyth; 6. Mary; 7. Gregg Allman; 8. Spain; 9. 17; 10. Swindon Town; 11. June; 12. Carl Lewis; 13. Mull; 14. Rome; 15. Earth, Wind and Fire; 16. Glenfiddich

QUIZ 246 (Science & Nature)

1. Lobster; 2. Lord (Martin) Rees; 3. Molluscs; 4. Kidney; 5. Daffodil; 6. Disease; 7. Mudskipper; 8. Brute; 9. Australia; 10. No, they glide; 11. Goliath frog; 12. Precious metals and gems; 13. Felix Wankel; 14. Viola; 15. Isaac Newton; 16. Ulna nerve

QUIZ 247

1. Lamborghini; 2. Simone de Beauvoir; 3. Tempura; 4. Kissing; 5. Nicaragua; 6. Pompadour; 7. Peter, a cat at Lord's; 8. Fleet; 9. Fountain; 10. Mary J Blige; 11. Music Of Black Origin; 12. Lubyanka; 13. Democratic People's Republic of Korea; 14. Pyongyang; 15. Edward VII; 16. Marcel Marceau

QUIZ 248

1. USA; 2. Venus Rosewater Dish; 3. Rupert Giles; 4. A, B, AB and O; 5. Kensington Palace; 6. Being overworked; 7. Catherine Cookson; 8. George II; 9. Five; 10. Gary Player; 11. Tay; 12. South African; 13. Cantons; 14. An inept boxer; 15. Vincent Van Gogh; 16. Alexandra Palace

QUIZ 249

1. Germany; 2. Peterloo; 3. Francis Bacon; 4. Chartwell; 5. Froghopper; 6. Denis Compton; 7. Polaroid; 8. Benjamin Franklin Pierce; 9. Clean slate; 10. Northwest Territories; 11. Avebury Circles; 12. 1900; 13. Roberts; 14. Polonius; 15. 1992; 16. Connecticut

QUIZ 250

1. Eyelid; 2. *Pacific Princess*; 3. 2000; 4. Robert Burns; 5. Sow; 6. Bobby Ball's; 7. Massachusetts; 8. Richard Dimbleby; 9. Sonny Bill Williams; 10. Spaniel; 11. Lloyd's; 12. Kenneth Lester (13-year-old rower); 13. Dartmoor; 14. Honolulu; 15. William Walton; 16. 1990

QUIZ 251

1. Benjamin Disraeli; 2. Henry Moore; 3. Four; 4. Ambush; 5. Michael Bloomberg; 6. Presto; 7. Helen Baxendale; 8. Karrie Webb; 9. Mt Pico (Pico Island); 10. Earl of Snowden; 11. Dr Kurt Waldheim; 12. *Ulysses* (James Joyce); 13. Gulf of Mexico; 14. *Tutti Frutti*; 15. Plum; 16. Darts

QUIZ 252

1. Olof Palme; 2. Sir Thomas More; 3. Majorca; 4. George Washington, Thomas Jefferson, Theodore Roosevelt, Abraham Lincoln; 5. William; 6. Rudyard Kipling; 7. Sun bear; 8. 26; 9. *Skylab*; 10. King Abdullah; 11. John Galsworthy; 12. Eric Bristow; 13. German; 14. Rocky Graziano; 15. Dover Street; 16. Ionian

QUIZ 253

1. Pat Jennngs; 2. Velocity; 3. Menachem Begin and Anwar Sadat; 4. Lei; 5. Cher; 6. *Manhattan Melodrama*; 7. Because of the USSR's invasion of Hungary; 8. Namib; 9. Edinburgh; 10. Aileen Quinn; 11. Josephine Baker; 12. *Breakfast Time*; 13. Selina Scott and Frank Bough; 14. 11; 15. Striptease artist; 16. Crooked sixpence

QUIZ 254 (Music)

1. Bon Jovi; 2. Julian Lennon; 3. *Lioness : Hidden Treasures*; 4. *Holiday Inn*;
5. 'Guantanamera'; 6. Sergei Prokofiev; 7. 88; 8. English and American
poetry; 9. Marian Anderson; 10. 14; 11. Foo Fighters; 12. 'Santa's List';
13. Noel Gallagher; 14. 'Rasputin'; 15. Tom Jones; 16. Elvis Presley

QUIZ 255

1. The Angry Brigade; 2. 77; 3. Mike Hailwood; 4. Wispy cirrus clouds;
5. Canal; 6. Timothy Lumsden; 7. Trevor Francis; 8. *Mr Lewisham*; 9. Ben
Johnson; 10. The Devonshires; 11. Shoaib Akhtar; 12. Green Line;
13. First female to ride in the Grand National; 14. Stephen Vincent
Benét; 15. Exeunt; 16. CAT scanner

QUIZ 256

1. Hockenheim; 2. Hugh Gaitskell; 3. Edmund Kean; 4. Justin Timberlake;
5. Book of Ruth and Book of Esther; 6. Racehorses; 7. Sedimentary;
8. Agent Zigzag; 9. Reginald Maudling; 10. Jamaica; 11. Yes (1900);
12. Regina; 13. Four; 14. Kulaks; 15. 40; 16. Timpani

QUIZ 257

1. Ben Affleck and Jennifer Lopez; 2. Canada; 3. Your teeth; 4. Plaster of
Paris; 5. Male; 6. Columbia University; 7. Joan Plowright; 8. TWA;
9. Sixpenny piece; 10. Arnold Palmer; 11. Luxembourg; 12. Princess
Anne; 13. Jason Donovan's; 14. Auguste and Jean-Felix Piccard;
15. Hungary; 16. Jack Kerouac

QUIZ 258

1. Aberdeen; 2. Brooke Shields; 3. Frankfurt; 4. Persian; 5. Andromeda;
6. Medicine; 7. John Dawes; 8. Marseille; 9. The Saint; 10. Ten
Commandments; 11. *Who Wants To Be A Millionaire?*; 12. Department
store; 13. Wycombe Wanderers; 14. Elvis Presley ('One Night'/'I Got
Stung'); 15. Borough Market; 16. 9am

QUIZ 259

1. Judith Keppel; 2. Doubloons; 3. Charlotte Edwards; 4. The Hubble;
5. Nathaniel Poe; 6. James Fenimore Cooper; 7. Jemini; 8. Bald Eagle;
9. Headgear; 10. Friday; 11. Pete Sampras; 12. Bilbao; 13. Leonard
Bernstein (Symphony No 2); 14. *Anschluss*; 15. Campania; 16. Charlie Drake

QUIZ 260

1. Columbia; 2. Access; 3. Hercules; 4. Bowler; 5. Computerised Axial
Tomography; 6. +353; 7. Squire Trelawney; 8. Lotus; 9. Portugal;
10. *Baedeker*; 11. Claude Debussy; 12. Zagreb (Croatia); 13. Hayley Atwell;
14. Four; 15. Montana; 16. Perfume

QUIZ 261 (History)

1. 15th; 2. Inca; 3. The British; 4. Andrew Bonar Law; 5. Wisconsin;
6. Manchester; 7. Gary Powers; 8. Lord Stansgate; 9. Austria; 10. Gerald
Ford; 11. Leicestershire; 12. The Prague Spring; 13. Albania; 14. George II;
15. 1938; 16. El Cid

QUIZ 262

1. Boxing kangaroo; 2. Poker; 3. Rachel Hunter; 4. Irn-Bru; 5. Rupert
Davies; 6. Merry or playful; 7. Frederick Forsyth; 8. Shinty; 9. Turban;
10. Knoll; 11. Copenhagen; 12. Heart attack; 13. Rita Coolidge;
14. Weymouth; 15. Yukio Mishima; 16. Billie Jean Moffitt

QUIZ 263

1. Albany; 2. David Beckham; 3. Argentina (1998); 4. Alfred, Lord
Tennyson; 5. Sweet Vermouth; 6. Princess Michael of Kent; 7. Banana;
8. Stork; 9. Nine; 10. Tim McInnerny; 11. Inflammation of the lungs;
12. Melbourne Park; 13. 1974; 14. Clay; 15. St Bride's; 16. Sophia

QUIZ 264

1. Benjamin Disraeli; 2. Kathryn; 3. Celtic; 4. Roman Catholic priests;
5. Battle of the Nile; 6. Birmingham; 7. Washington DC; 8. France and

Italy; 9. Smarties; 10. Lord Kitchener; 11. Jack Wild; 12. Lehman Brothers; 13. Mario Vargas Llosa; 14. Market garden; 15. Moth; 16. Portsmouth

QUIZ 265

1. *Father Ted*; 2. Sarah; 3. Judy Blackamoor; 4. The Press (or news media); 5. Jackie Kennedy; 6. John Bull; 7. Metamorphosis; 8. Rhubarb; 9. Ireland's; 10. Laertes; 11. The slowest; 12. Queen Elizabeth (consort of George VI); 13. Australia; 14. Brain; 15. Coventry City; 16. Treaty of Paris

QUIZ 266

1. China; 2. Jamaica; 3. The Philippines; 4. St Alban; 5. Catkin; 6. Kentucky Fried Chicken; 7. Jamie Cox; 8. Cheryl Hines; 9. Flying circus; 10. Izaak Walton; 11. 'For valour'; 12. Leila Williams; 13. Wampum; 14. Mrs Fox; 15. Parc du Champ de Mars; 16. Wales

QUIZ 267

1. Moorgate station; 2. Betty Stove; 3. Brian Keenan; 4. Among other things; 5. Princess Margaret; 6. Eric Spear; 7. Joyce Smith; 8. Telly; 9. Popular English novelist at the turn of the 20th century; 10. Margaret Mead; 11. Erica Roe; 12. Chepstow; 13. Belgium; 14. John Adams; 15. Hats; 16. Lyon

QUIZ 268

1. T S Eliot; 2. General Naguib; 3. Beggar; 4. Fort William; 5. Lotus; 6. Papeete; 7. Mike Hawthorn; 8. Police Community Support Officer; 9. Newcastle; 10. Connecticut; 11. Artois; 12. Tax collector; 13. 1843; 14. Colon; 15. Right; 16. Fluke

QUIZ 269 (Geography)

1. Balboa; 2. South Dakota; 3. Australia's; 4. Argentina; 5. Yorkshire; 6. Corfu; 7. Canada; 8. Orinoco; 9. Brussels; 10. Oakham; 11. Stewart Island; 12. Australian tropical cyclone; 13. Lake Constance; 14. Stockholm; 15. Forest; 16. Longships

QUIZ 270

1. Bond girls; 2. Dr Crippen; 3. They are equal; 4. Montélimar; 5. Pelé;
6. Mussel; 7. Florida; 8. John McEnroe; 9. John Denver's; 10. Bridge;
11. Gerald Ford's; 12. Westminster Abbey; 13. Hat; 14. Speedway;
15. Côtes du Rhône; 16. Leonard

QUIZ 271

1. BBC Symphony; 2. 14; 3. Rawalpindi; 4. Geraldine James; 5. Gaetano
Donizetti; 6. *Départements*; 7. Manhattan; 8. Richard Burton; 9. Boursin;
10. Attila the Hun; 11. Becoming phobic; 12. *Quadrophenia*; 13. Pathan;
14. Spiked helmet; 15. 4am; 16. 25

QUIZ 272

1. 11; 2. Three; 3. Jean Claude Van Damme; 4. Oxford; 5. Georgia;
6. Mediterranean; 7. Georges Clemenceau; 8. Diamonds; 9. China's;
10. Julius Caesar and Cleopatra; 11. Rugby league; 12. *Treasure Island*
(1950); 13. Bobby Driscoll; 14. Mrs (Cathy) Gale; 15. Back; 16. Grenada

QUIZ 273

1. St Geneviève; 2. American; 3. Red; 4. Alcohol; 5. 47; 6. Leyton Orient;
7. 960; 8. Georgi Malenkov; 9. Orange; 10. Cairo; 11. US advertising;
12. Lewis; 13. Ed Balls and Yvette Cooper; 14. Crow; 15. *Cat on a Hot Tin
Roof*; 16. F R Brown

QUIZ 274

1. Six; 2. Paris; 3. Odysseus and Penelope; 4. Five; 5. 'All I Want For
Christmas Is My Two Front Teeth'; 6. Earache; 7. Saints; 8. Germany;
9. *Macbeth*; 10. Glenn Hoddle; 11. Tiergarten; 12. Clearing House
Automated Payment System (CHAPS); 13. Hibernia; 14. Tibet; 15. The
tanker *Exxon Valdez*; 16. Louella

QUIZ 275

1. Robson Green; 2. Water is formed; 3. Banker; 4. Yul Brynner;
5. Chandler; 6. Diet; 7. Tutankhamun; 8. Emperor Haile Selassie I of
Ethiopia; 9. Simon and Garfunkel's; 10. Maquis; 11. India; 12. Gene
Cernan (*Apollo 11*); 13. David Mitchell's; 14. Jan Koller; 15. Song thrush;
16. 56

QUIZ 276 (Sport)

1. Australia; 2. 16; 3. De Boer; 4. The America's Cup (1851); 5. Fred
Archer; 6. Sir Brian Lochore; 7. Ross County; 8. Bobsleighing;
9. Stockholm (1912); 10. 136; 11. Italian; 12. Each captained England 90
times; 13. Bowls; 14. Three; 15. Abraham Benjamin; 16. Chris Amon

QUIZ 277

1. Ian Botham's; 2. *The Taming of the Shrew*; 3. 1979; 4. Jeremy Vine;
5. Pb; 6. 115; 7. John Sentamu; 8. Petals; 9. Robert Louis Stevenson;
10. The Rockies; 11. Spencer Perceval; 12. Marshal Blücher; 13. Dr Alfred
Kinsey; 14. 38; 15. Ho Chi Minh; 16. East Pakistan

QUIZ 278

1. (J K) Galbraith; 2. San Simeon; 3. Hawaii; 4. Amphibians; 5. Sago;
6. Norway's; 7. Joanne Woodward; 8. National Government; 9. Benjamin
Disraeli; 10. Pelican crossings; 11. Algeria; 12. *Pan Am*; 13. Creates sound
effects; 14. Entr'acte; 15. Mary Robinson; 16. Advocaat

QUIZ 279

1. Dermot Morgan; 2. Colin Cowdrey; 3. California's list of top tax
evaders; 4. Powys; 5. Egyptian and Greek; 6. 61 (Joshua Millner, 1908);
7. Shooting; 8. 18th Century; 9. Vanuatu; 10. Oliver Cromwell;
11. Fae; 12. Steel; 13. Nigel Lawson; 14. Father Divine's; 15. 1984;
16. Al Swearengen

QUIZ 280

1. Margaret Beckett; 2. *Come Fly With Me*; 3. Gordon Richards;
4. Menagerie; 5. Second Book of Kings; 6. Elizabeth David's; 7. Australian mainland and Tasmania; 8. Cleveland, Ohio; 9. Stealth bomber;
10. Herbert Asquith; 11. *Cantina*; 12. Harold Pinter's; 13. Swiss;
14. Carthage; 15. William Burroughs; 16. Abseilling

QUIZ 281

1. Blue elephant called Stumpy; 2. Ray Davies; 3. Audi; 4. Tim Roth;
5. New; 6. 90%; 7. One; 8. *Golden Hind*; 9. Lead; 10. Henry; 11. The Eagles;
12. None; 13. Lieutenant general; 14. Geothermal; 15. French horn;
16. *Slainte*

QUIZ 282

1. Martina Hingis; 2. St Giles; 3. Harry Truman; 4. *News of the World*'s;
5. Edouard Manet; 6. Dennis Lillee; 7. Donkey; 8. Edward I of England;
9. Lester Piggott; 10. Pamela Anderson; 11. Takla Makan; 12. Five billion;
13. Luxembourg; 14. Australia and West Indies; 15. Its bicentenary;
16. Philip II

QUIZ 283

1. 42 days; 2. Chicken; 3. Herbert Hoover and Richard Nixon; 4. Someone who loves money; 5. South Africa; 6. Amalgum; 7. Kigali; 8. Coco Chanel;
9. Mark Chapman; 10. Lines of the same length; 11. Paul McCartney;
12. Norway; 13. Plymouth, Massachusetts; 14. Paris St Germain;
15. Shekel; 16. 325 days

QUIZ 284 (Cinema & TV)

1. Winchester Club; 2. *Ordinary People*; 3. Vienna; 4. Daniel Day-Lewis;
5. Sonny and Cher's 'I Got You Babe'; 6. *8*; 7. Art and Maths;
8. Tweedledum and Tweedledee; 9. Robin Day; 10. *Softly, Softly*; 11. 22;
12. Sherlock Holmes; 13. *Dr No*; 14. Daisy, Rose, Violet; 15. Sam Mendes;
16. Esther

QUIZ 285

1. The Bends; 2. Calvin Coolidge; 3. In a science lab; 4. *Fromagerie*;
5. Chet Baker; 6. Marco Polo; 7. Silvio Berlusconi; 8. 'Witchfinder
General'; 9. Michelle Williams; 10. Their manager Brian Epstein;
11. Berti Vogts; 12. Sweden; 13. 1945; 14. Blood; 15. Sean Connery;
16. Colombia

QUIZ 286

1. Peter Davison; 2. Henry II; 3. Pachyderm; 4. Sisal fibres; 5. Diane
Cilento; 6. Germany; 7. Papal Legate; 8. *GoldenEye*; 9. Curling;
10. 'Christmas Auld Lang Syne'; 11. Bombardier Billy Wells; 12. Annie in
Little Orphan Annie; 13. Tribute; 14. Little black dress; 15. Harry Vardon;
16. A food poisoning scare

QUIZ 287

1. *Student* magazine; 2. Trevor Baylis; 3. Reg Harris; 4. 'I have found it';
5. Caspar Weinberger; 6. *Look Back in Anger*; 7. Buckwheat;
8. Switzerland; 9. *The Reader*; 10. Bratislava; 11. Seven; 12. The Queen;
13. Wig; 14. 70; 15. Montmorency; 16. Mesopotamia

QUIZ 288

1. El Salvador and Honduras; 2. *The London Gazette*; 3. Vasco da Gama;
4. Tony Starks'; 5. Red; 6. 20; 7. Gin; 8. Moon River; 9. 20; 10. Giant Eland;
11. Whales and dolphins; 12. 30 days; 13. *Her Lover*; 14. Portree;
15. Vivian Fuchs; 16. Cowes Week

QUIZ 289

1. At home; 2. Rudy Giuliani; 3. Molotov (cocktail); 4. Nanette Newman;
5. 8ft x 8yd (2.4m x 7.3m); 6. Taransay; 7. Seven; 8. The seven continents
and the seven seas; 9. Edward Kennedy; 10. Mezzo soprano; 11. Dubai;
12. Comedy; 13. Bernie Taupin; 14. Britain, France and Russia; 15. John
Reid; 16. Jack Nicholson

QUIZ 290

1. Imperial State Crown; 2. Smithsonian; 3. Washington DC; 4. Dogs;
5. Gustav Klimt; 6. Marcel Desailly; 7. Professor Alan Walters; 8. Brighton
& Hove Albion; 9. Daphne du Maurier; 10. Denmark's; 11. Barack Obama;
12. General William Slim; 13. Logistics; 14. Six; 15. Tiny Tim; 16. Jupiter

QUIZ 291 (Science & Nature)

1. Colours; 2. Robotic 'moon-walker'; 3. Mayfly; 4. Hg; 5. Wanderer;
6. Sex; 7. Protein catalyst; 8. Pierre de Fermat; 9. Seven;
10. Rhododendron; 11. Tendon; 12. Humidity; 13. By sucking;
14. Jurassic; 15. Marsupials; 16. Sharp point or pinnacle of rock

QUIZ 292

1. Paragon; 2. Hecate; 3. Roland Butcher; 4. Gemstones; 5. *Eldorado*;
6. Key Largo; 7. China; 8. James J Braddock; 9. Centenary of Thomas
Edison's invention of sound recording; 10. Shinty; 11. Dame Commander
of the Order of St Michael and St George; 12. Dawn French's;
13. Narcissus; 14. Eric; 15. Benito Mussolini's; 16. *The Pickwick Papers*

QUIZ 293

1. Open University; 2. Yellow; 3. On the other hand; 4. *Roman Holiday*;
5. Alan Ball; 6. L'Aquila; 7. FIFA World Cup; 8. Willy Brandt; 9. The Four
Tops; 10. Prince and Princess Michael of Kent's; 11. The prime minister
of the day; 12. Elephant; 13. Scott; 14. Robert Penn Warren's;
15. Frank Muir and Denis Norden; 16. 1937

QUIZ 294

1. Vulcanizing; 2. Harold Wilson; 3. Myalgic encephalomyelitis; 4. Five;
5. Bangladesh; 6. Gentoo penguin; 7. Richard Attenborough's;
8. Congress of Vienna; 9. Under the centre circle of Stoke City's ground;
10. South; 11. Scat; 12. Cleveland, Ohio; 13. Paving stone; 14. Plainsong;
15. Doctor; 16. Confluence

QUIZ 295

1. *Gambas*; 2. 'Handbags And Gladrags'; 3. Calvin Klein; 4. Gnasher;
5. Madrid; 6. Bill Wyman; 7. Reading's; 8. The appropriate word;
9. Three; 10. Breed of terrier; 11. Lee; 12. Macramé; 13. Strontium (after
Strontian); 14. Tanzania; 15. Valley or ravine; 16. The Breakfast Club

QUIZ 296

1. David Brent; 2. He scored his maiden Test century there; 3. Amber;
4. Four; 5. Tony Blair's; 6. Robert Wagner; 7. Magna Carta; 8. Tunisia;
9. Brain waves; 10. Barry John; 11. Polygraph; 12. Senator John Kerry;
13. Bill Haley and the Comets; 14. Cecil B De Mille's; 15. The Niger;
16. Yeovil Town

QUIZ 297

1. *Fleur-de-lis*; 2. Aaron Copland; 3. Pfennig; 4. 40 days; 5. Female;
6. Afghanistan and Pakistan; 7. 'Place of the Massacre'; 8. Bivalves;
9. Amerigo Vespucci; 10. May Britt; 11. Gloucester; 12. *The Passion of the
Christ* (Mel Gibson); 13. A sound installation (by Susan Philipsz);
14. (D W) Griffith; 15. Liège; 16. 75

QUIZ 298

1. Ponzi scheme; 2. Tibet; 3. Princess Anne; 4. Nano; 5. Cocktail glasses;
6. 1944; 7. Ralph Bunche (1950); 8. *The Trial*; 9. François Truffaut;
10. Duke of Hamilton; 11. Safety pin; 12. *Molly*; 13. 'It ain't over till the
fat lady sings'; 14. US Library of Congress; 15. Lindisfarne; 16. PX

QUIZ 299 (Music)

1. Oasis'; 2. Faust; 3. Labelle; 4. Kanya King; 5. *American Gigolo*; 6. *Taylor
Swift*; 7. *Lulu*; 8. Fantine; 9. Britney Spears; 10. 'Here Come The Girls';
11. George Martin; 12. Lorenz Hart; 13. *Four Weddings and a Funeral*;
14. Lulu; 15. Elton John; 16. Paul Weller

QUIZ 300

1. Australia; 2. Water; 3. Arctic Circle; 4. 1961; 5. Keith Miller; 6. 'Take My Breath Away'; 7. Berlin; 8. Houston; 9. Gin and brandy; 10. Roland Kirk; 11. Kelsey Grammer; 12. *David Copperfield*; 13. The Titan (Derbyshire); 14. Dan; 15. Basque; 16. Croatia's

QUIZ 301

1. Angela Merkel; 2. First mate; 3. Kaka; 4. Elections and voting trends; 5. French writer George Sand's; 6. Cucumber; 7. Paul Henreid; 8. Napster; 9. Barry Goldwater; 10. Perkin Warbeck; 11. Talcum powder; 12. Canaan Banana; 13. Poult; 14. Antarctica; 15. Ullswater; 16. Mark Twain

QUIZ 302

1. India; 2. Lord Liverpool; 3. Colchester; 4. Ears, nose and throat; 5. American football; 6. Dionysus; 7. Dalai Lama's; 8. Luddites; 9. Wales; 10. Sled; 11. Beastie Boys; 12. Obtuse; 13. Kim Philby; 14. 24; 15. Carrara; 16. Bing Crosby's

QUIZ 303

1. Alan Shearer; 2. Duke of Windsor; 3. Elmore Leonard; 4. Boomerang; 5. Tonga's; 6. Drowned trying to swim the rapids at Niagara Falls; 7. Mimi; 8. Bask; 9. Hugo Boss; 10. Romania; 11. Sizes of paper; 12. Geoff Cooke; 13. Willy Brandt; 14. Heracles; 15. 1787; 16. Richard Rogers

QUIZ 304

1. Green; 2. Salvation Army's; 3. Potassium; 4. Epidemiology; 5. Wing forward; 6. Heraldry; 7. In a fire; 8. Canada; 9. Amsterdam; 10. Hawaii; 11. Gary Waldhorn; 12. Northern Territory; 13. *Ryan's Daughter*; 14. 167; 15. Institute of Contemporary Arts; 16. Calamity Jane

QUIZ 305

1. Apollo; 2. 175; 3. Carpenter; 4. South Korean; 5. Manatee; 6. Los Angeles (1984); 7. Washington DC; 8. Aix-la-Chapelle; 9. Nigeria;